Score a top SATS mark with CGP!

This fantastic CGP book is fully up-to-date for the new KS2 Maths SATS in 2016 and beyond!

It's packed with realistic SATS-style questions covering all the most difficult Year 6 Maths topics.

There are also Practice Tests at the start and the end of the book — perfect for measuring how much progress they've made.

What CGP is all about

Our sole aim here at CGP is to produce the highest quality books — carefully written, immaculately presented and dangerously close to being funny.

Then we work our socks off to get them out to you — at the cheapest possible prices.

Contents

Published by CGP

Editors:
Joanna Daniels, Rob Harrison, Shaun Harrogate, Sharon Keeley-Holden, Caley Simpson

Contributor:
Sue Foord

ISBN: 978 1 78294 420 1

With thanks to Kirstie McHale and Tina Ramsden for the proofreading.
Also thanks to Laura Jakubowski for the copyright research.

Thumb illustration used throughout the book © iStockphoto.com.

Contains public sector information licensed under the Open Government Licence v3.0.
http://www.nationalarchives.gov.uk/doc/open-government-licence/version/3/

Printed by Elanders Ltd, Newcastle upon Tyne.
Clipart from Corel®

About This Book

This Book is Full of KS2 Maths Questions

At the end of Year 6, you'll be tested on all the maths you've learnt during Key Stage 2.

This book has questions on the harder topics you might be tested on.

This book also has two Practice Tests.
The one at the front of the book is to test how much you already know.
The test at the back of the book is to see how much more you can do after using this book.

The answers to all of the questions are at the back of this book.

> This book covers all the Learning Objectives for Year 6 of the National Curriculum.

This Book Matches Our Advanced Revision Book

The Advanced Revision Book can help you if you get stuck.
It explains all the maths you need to know to get top marks on your test.
It's also got worked examples to show you how to answer test questions.

There are Learning Objectives on All Pages

Learning objectives say what you should be able to do.
Use the tick circles to show how confident you feel.

Tick here if you think you need a bit more practice.

If you're really struggling, tick here.

Tick this circle if you can do all the maths on the page.

"I can multiply a four-digit number by a two-digit number."

Practice Test 1

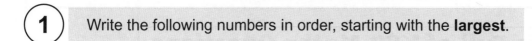

1 Write the following numbers in order, starting with the **largest**.

54 300   53 400   540 300   504 030

largest   smallest

1 mark

2 This table shows the number of people who attended a football match.

Complete the table by rounding the number of people to the given amount.

Number of people	Rounded to nearest 10	Rounded to nearest 100	Rounded to nearest 1000
47 346			

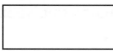

2 marks

3 Calculate 675 × 38.

1 mark

4 This question is about fractions.

Write the missing numbers in the boxes.

$$\frac{2}{3} = \frac{\square}{12} \qquad \frac{8}{\square} = \frac{1}{2}$$

1 mark

Calculate the following. Give your answer as a mixed number.

$$\frac{3}{4} + \frac{2}{3}$$

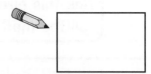

1 mark

5 A couple need 185 invitations for their wedding.
The invitations are sold in packs of 12.

How many packs must they buy?

6 This regular pentagon is made from five identical isosceles triangles.

Calculate angles x and y.

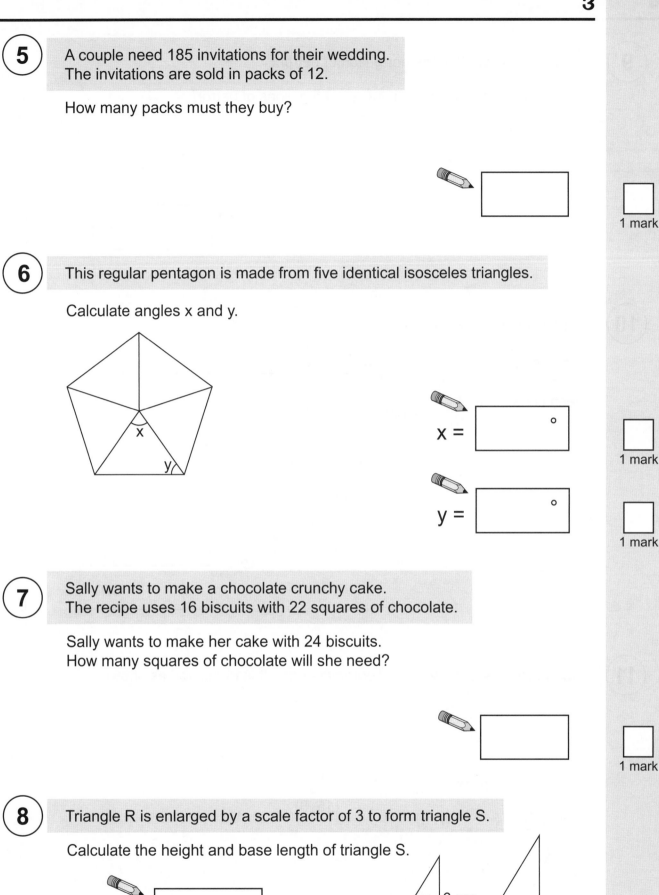

x = ____ °

y = ____ °

7 Sally wants to make a chocolate crunchy cake.
The recipe uses 16 biscuits with 22 squares of chocolate.

Sally wants to make her cake with 24 biscuits.
How many squares of chocolate will she need?

8 Triangle R is enlarged by a scale factor of 3 to form triangle S.

Calculate the height and base length of triangle S.

Height = ____ cm

Base = ____ cm

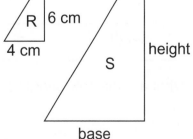

R 6 cm

4 cm

S height

base

4

9 A car can travel 40 **miles** per gallon of petrol.

How many **kilometres** can it travel on 5 gallons of petrol?

| km |

10 Here is the net of a cuboid.

What is the volume of
the cuboid after it has
been constructed?

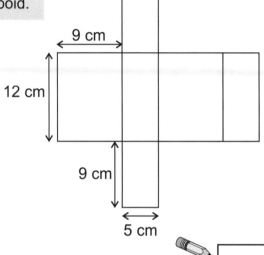

| cm³ |

11 Quadrilateral A is drawn on a coordinate grid. It is translated as shown.

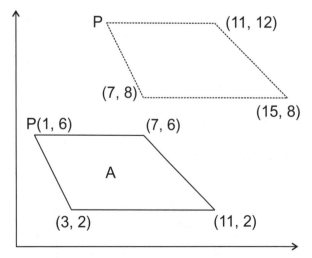

What are the new coordinates of point P?

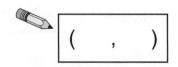

(,   )

12 A laptop normally sells for £290. It is in the sale at 20% off.

What is the sale price of the laptop?

£ ☐

2 marks

13 A baker sells fruit cakes for £7 each and sponge cakes for £4 each.

He calculates his earnings (E) using the equation:

E = 7f + 4s

where f is the number of fruit cakes sold
and s is the number of sponge cakes sold.

In one hour he sold 6 fruit cakes and 9 sponge cakes.
How much did he earn?

£ ☐

1 mark

14 Simon bought a bag of sweets. A third of the sweets were red.
There were equal amounts of black and green sweets.
A quarter of the sweets were orange, and the rest were yellow.

Label the pie chart to show which
sector represents each colour.
One has been done for you.

green

1 mark

There were 24 sweets in Simon's bag. How many were green?

1 mark

Total ☐

Practice Test 1

Ordering Numbers

(1) A football player is sold for eight million, four hundred and sixty three thousand, seven hundred pounds.

Write this amount as a number.

£

1 mark

(2) Write out the number 28 740 827 in words.

1 mark

(3) In the number 17 052 826, the 8 represents 800.

What does the 7 represent in figures?

What does the 5 represent in figures?

1 mark

(4) Redland and Blueland are two countries. The population of Redland is 9 643 174. The population of Blueland is nine million, six hundred and forty two thousand, one hundred and fifty.

Which country has the largest population?

1 mark

Ordering Numbers

5 Fill in the missing number in the following calculation.

$$1\ 070\ 350\ =\ 1\ 000\ 000\ +\ \boxed{}\ +\ 300\ +\ 50$$

1 mark

6 Write the following numbers in **descending** order.

15 023 223   15 024 764   15 023 096   15 024 888

largest

smallest

1 mark

7 Here are eight numbered cards.

| 8 | 3 | 9 | 4 | 3 | 7 | 5 | 8 |

What is the largest number you can make using all the cards?

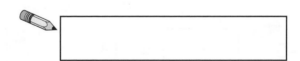

1 mark

What is the smallest **even** number you can make using all the cards?

1 mark

"I can read, write, order and
compare numbers up to ten million,
and work out the value of each digit."

SECTION ONE — NUMBER & PLACE VALUE

Negative Numbers

1 Work out each of these calculations. Use the number line to help you.

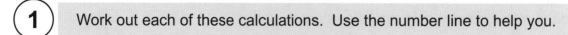

$$5 - 8 = \boxed{} \qquad -3 + 12 = \boxed{}$$

1 mark

2 Nina writes a sequence of numbers.

Write down the next two numbers in Nina's sequence.

50   35   20   5    $\boxed{} \quad \boxed{}$

1 mark

3 Phil is in a lift. The lift says he is on floor –2.

The lift goes up 18 floors. What floor is Phil on now?
Use this number line to help you.

 $\boxed{}$

1 mark

4 Fill in the missing numbers to make the following calculations correct.

$$-5 - \boxed{} = -18 \qquad \boxed{} + 9 = -3$$

1 mark

5 Katya measured the temperature in her garden as –6 °C before she went to school and 11 °C when she got back from school.

What was the difference between Katya's
two temperature measurements?

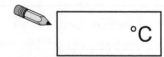 $\boxed{}$ °C

1 mark

Negative Numbers

---

(6) The amount of money in three bank accounts is shown on the right.

Name	Bank Balance
Xavier	–£88
Sophia	£32
Mya	–£28

Xavier pays £150 into his account.
What is his bank balance now?

 £ ☐

1 mark

What is the difference between
Sophia's bank balance and Mya's bank balance?

 £ ☐

1 mark

(7) Make each of the following calculations correct using **one** = sign and **one** of the operations + or – .

 –8 ☐ 3 ☐ –5

 –17 ☐ –10 ☐ 7

1 mark

(8) Annabel writes a sequence of numbers. She adds 18 each time.

Fill in the two missing numbers in Annabel's sequence.

 ☐ –50 –32 –14 ☐

1 mark

"I can calculate using negative numbers."

Section One — Number & Place Value

Rounding Off

1 Round each of these numbers.

25 547 to the nearest hundred

508 647 to the nearest thousand

1 mark

2 Fill in the gaps in the sentences below.

78 705 rounded to the nearest _____ is 78 700.

1 mark

987 537 rounded to the nearest _____ is 990 000.

1 mark

3 By rounding each number to the nearest thousand, estimate the answer to 8672 + 7239.

1 mark

4 Round each of these numbers to the nearest million.

17 950 254 ⟶

29 045 444 ⟶

1 mark

Rounding Off

5 Circle the decimal that is 3.545 rounded to 2 decimal places.

3.50   3.54   3.60   3.55

1 mark

6 Round each of these numbers to 1 decimal place.

25.548   49.982

1 mark

7 Three boys each ran one lap of a three lap race. Their lap times were 47.378 seconds, 38.746 seconds and 34.970 seconds.

By rounding each time to the nearest 10 seconds, estimate the total time it took the boys to complete the race.

seconds

2 marks

8 Manjit weighed two letters. The first letter weighed 15.653 grams and the second letter weighed 23.064 grams.

By rounding the weight of each letter to 1 decimal place, estimate the total weight of both letters.

grams

2 marks

"I can round any whole number.
I can round decimal numbers to a
given number of decimal places."

Section One — Number & Place Value

Written Multiplication

(1) Pencils come in boxes of 20.

How many pencils are there in 1500 boxes?

1 mark

(2) Fill in the missing numbers in the calculation below.

$$
\begin{array}{r}
2\ 7 \\
\times\ 1\ 5 \\
\hline
\boxed{}\ 3\ \boxed{} \\
2\ \boxed{}\ 0 \\
\hline
\boxed{} \\
\end{array}
$$

1 mark

(3) What is 374 × 23?

2 marks

(4) Each day, David uses 16 grams of yeast to make bread.

There are 365 days in a year.
How many grams of yeast will he use in a year?

grams

2 marks

Written Multiplication

5 Fill in the missing digits in these calculations.

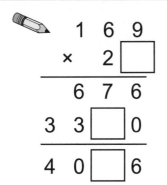

```
      1  6  9
   ×     2 ☐
   ─────────────
      6  7  6
   3  3 ☐  0
   ─────────────
   4  0 ☐  6
```

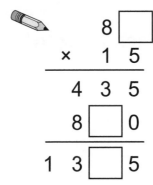

```
         8 ☐
   ×  1  5
   ─────────────
   4  3  5
   8 ☐  0
   ─────────────
   1  3 ☐  5
```

6 Calculate:

4723 × 61   3816 × 44

7 The table below shows some information about an annual running race. All of the runners finished the race in both years.

Year	Race distance (km)	Number of runners
2013	20	2589
2014	42	750

What was the total distance run by all the runners in 2013 and 2014?

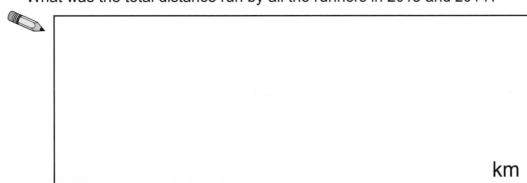

km

"I can multiply a four-digit number by a two-digit number."

Written Division

1 Circle the correct answer to 4374 ÷ 9.

356   396   466   486

2 12 bakers each bake the same number of cakes.
The total number of cakes baked is 756.

How many cakes does each baker make?

3 Fill in the missing digits to make these divisions correct.

$$11 \overline{)\ 7\ 4\ 8}$$

$$8 \overline{)\ \square\ 5\ 5\ 2}$$ 6 9 □

4 What is 6384 ÷ 21?

5 What number multiplies by 12 to give 4404?

Written Division

6 Becky is using a 408 cm length of string to make some bracelets. She uses 15 cm of string for each bracelet.

How many bracelets can she make?

How much string will be left over?

cm

7 What is the remainder when 7592 is divided by 22?

8 There are 29 pupils in Class 6A. The teacher brings in a huge bag containing 3842 sweets. The teacher shares the sweets equally among all the pupils and keeps the remaining sweets for herself.

How many sweets does the teacher get?

"I can divide a four-digit number by a two-digit number and know what to do with remainders."

Multiplying and Dividing with Decimals

1 Draw lines to match each calculation with the correct answer.

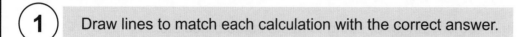

6.82 × 1000	6820
6.82 ÷ 10	0.0682
6.82 × 100	682
6.82 ÷ 100	0.682

1 mark

2 Work out each of these calculations.

0.4 × 12 = ⬜   8.1 ÷ 9 = ⬜

2 marks

3 Jared buys 7 cinema tickets for £3.80 each.

How much does Jared pay in total?

£

1 mark

4 A drainage pipe is made up of 8 plastic tubes joined end to end.
Each plastic tube is 1.68 metres long.

How long is the drainage pipe?

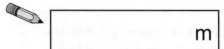

m

1 mark

Multiplying and Dividing with Decimals

5 A farmer delivers 261.8 litres of milk each week.
He delivers the same amount of milk on each day of the week.

How many litres of milk does he deliver each day?

litres

6 What is 59.36 ÷ 14?

7 A ferry can travel a distance of 16.84 miles in 1 hour.

How far can the ferry travel in 5 hours?

miles

How far can the ferry travel in 15 minutes?

miles

"I can multiply and divide
decimal numbers by whole numbers."

Order of Operations

1 Calculate:

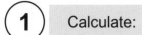

$8 + 9 \times 2 =$ ☐

$12 - 8 \div 4 =$ ☐

2 Draw lines to match up calculations with the same answer.

$8 + 2 \times 8$

$(5 \times 6) \div 3$

$9 \div 3 - 6$

$9 - 3 \times 4$

$8 + 8 \div 4$

$(7 + 5) \times 2$

3 Paulo has 6 packets of biscuits, each containing 14 biscuits.
He shares the biscuits between himself and 20 of his friends.

How many biscuits does each person get?

4 Jane has 2 dogs. Each of them eats 3 packets of dog food a day.
Packets of dog food come in boxes of 5.

How many boxes does Jane need to buy to feed her dogs for a week?

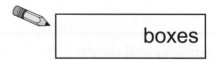 boxes

Order of Operations

5 Daniel and Stacey are working out how much they spent on sausage rolls at a bakery last year. Daniel spent £32.24 and bought 26 sausage rolls.

Stacey bought 17 sausage rolls. How much did they cost her?

£ _____

2 marks

6 The table on the right shows the price of some items at a stationery shop.

Tristan buys six of each item.
How much change does he get from £10?

Stationery Shop Prices	
Pencils	24p
Pens	70p
Rubbers	35p

£ _____

2 marks

7 At the local shop, yoghurts cost 19p each and apples cost 22p each.

Emily has £5 and she buys 12 yoghurts.
What is the maximum number of apples she can buy?

_____

2 marks

"I can work out what calculations I need to use to solve a problem. I know the order to do things in a calculation."

Estimation and Accuracy

1 By using estimation, circle the correct answer to 810.24 ÷ 38.4.

34.8   58.9   21.1   14.3

1 mark

2 Estimate the answer to (312 × 19) ÷ 5.8.

1 mark

3 Use estimation to show that the answer to 33.549 ÷ 6 is between 5 and 6.

1 mark

4 Phoebe works out that (9.75 × 25.14) − 10.115 = 189.

Is Phoebe correct? Explain your answer using estimation.

1 mark

"I can estimate to check the
answer to a calculation."

Factors, Multiples and Primes

1 Find all the factors of 72.

1 mark

2 Circle all the numbers in the list below that are multiples of **both** 6 and 8.

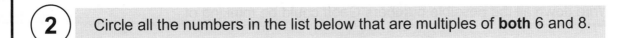

12   24   36   48   62   72   80

1 mark

3 Write down all the prime numbers between 40 and 50.

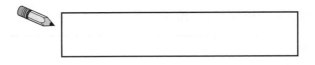

2 marks

4 Write down all the common factors of 36 and 54.

2 marks

5 Write a prime number in each box to make this calculation correct.

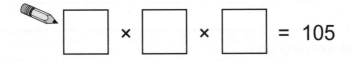

$$\boxed{} \times \boxed{} \times \boxed{} = 105$$

1 mark

Factors, Multiples and Primes

6 Find two common multiples of 6 and 9 between 1 and 50.

[   ] and [   ]

1 mark

7 Geoff is thinking of a number. The number is prime and a factor of 52.

Write down all the possible numbers Geoff could be thinking of.

[   ]

2 marks

8 A perfect number is a number that is equal to the sum of its factors (except the number itself). For example, 1, 2, 3 and 6 are the factors of 6, and 6 = 1 + 2 + 3.

Is 28 a perfect number? Explain your answer.

1 mark

9 Adele says, "Adding two prime numbers together always gives an even number."

Give an example showing that Adele's statement is wrong.

1 mark

"I know how to find common multiples, common factors and prime numbers."

Fractions

1 Circle any fractions below that are equivalent to $\frac{2}{3}$.

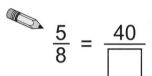
$\frac{3}{6}$ $\frac{6}{9}$ $\frac{6}{8}$ $\frac{4}{9}$ $\frac{8}{12}$

1 mark

2 Fill in the boxes to make each pair of fractions equivalent.

$\frac{5}{8} = \frac{40}{\Box}$ $\frac{4}{7} = \frac{\Box}{21}$ $\frac{2}{\Box} = \frac{18}{45}$

2 marks

3 Simplify each fraction as much as possible.

$\frac{12}{66} = \frac{\Box}{\Box}$ $\frac{36}{96} = \frac{\Box}{\Box}$ $\frac{121}{88} = \frac{\Box}{\Box}$

2 marks

4 Pippa has a grid divided into 20 squares. She shades 9 squares. Kai has a grid divided into 100 squares.

How many squares does he need to shade so that the same fraction of his grid is shaded?

1 mark

5 Write equivalent fractions for both of the fractions below using the same denominator.

$\frac{8}{9}$ and $\frac{13}{12}$

$\dfrac{}{}$ and $\dfrac{}{}$

2 marks

"I can simplify fractions.
I can write equivalent fractions
with the same denominator."

Comparing Fractions

(1) Put the fractions below in order from smallest to largest.

$$\frac{4}{3} \qquad \frac{5}{6} \qquad \frac{10}{9} \qquad \frac{17}{18}$$

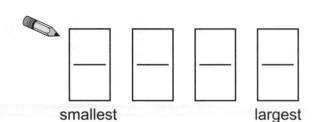

smallest   largest

1 mark

(2) Put the fractions below in order from largest to smallest.

$$\frac{3}{4} \qquad \frac{8}{9} \qquad \frac{5}{6} \qquad \frac{7}{12}$$

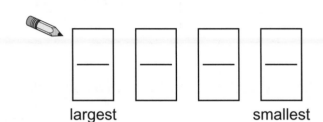

largest   smallest

1 mark

(3) For each pair of fractions below, circle the **larger** value.

$$\frac{5}{6} \text{ and } \frac{13}{15} \qquad\qquad \frac{11}{8} \text{ and } \frac{23}{20} \qquad\qquad 1\frac{5}{7} \text{ and } \frac{7}{4}$$

2 marks

(4) Emily, Max and Ahmed each have a pizza of the same size.

Emily's pizza was cut into eighths, and she has eaten 5 slices.
Max's pizza was cut into sixths, and he has eaten 4 slices.
Ahmed's pizza was cut into quarters, and he has eaten 3 slices.

Who has eaten the most pizza? Show your working.

2 marks

"I can compare and order fractions,
including fractions greater than 1."

Multiplying Fractions

1 Calculate:

$$\frac{1}{6} \times \frac{1}{4}$$

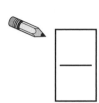

$$\frac{1}{11} \times \frac{1}{5}$$

2 What is $\frac{4}{9} \times \frac{2}{9}$?

3 Calculate $\frac{2}{5} \times \frac{3}{4}$. Give your answer in its simplest form.

4 Fill in the missing numbers in the calculations below.

$$\frac{4}{5} \times \frac{1}{\square} = \frac{\square}{15}$$

$$\frac{\square}{3} \times \frac{4}{\square} = \frac{8}{21}$$

"I can multiply fractions by other fractions."

SECTION THREE — FRACTIONS, DECIMALS & PERCENTAGES

Adding and Subtracting Fractions

1 Calculate:

$$\frac{2}{5} + \frac{7}{15}$$

$$\frac{2}{3} - \frac{11}{18}$$

2 marks

2 Work out the answer to the sum below.
Give your answer as a mixed number.

$$\frac{9}{8} + \frac{1}{5}$$

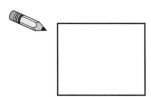

1 mark

3 Rosie has made $1\frac{3}{10}$ litres of orange squash.
She gives $\frac{5}{8}$ of a litre of orange squash to Owen.

How much orange squash does Rosie have left?

litres

2 marks

4 Work out the sum below.

Give your answer as a mixed number in its simplest form.

$$1\frac{3}{4} + 1\frac{1}{6}$$

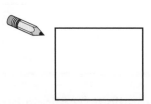

2 marks

<u>Adding and Subtracting Fractions</u>

5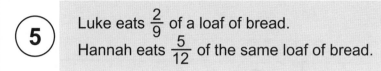

Luke eats $\frac{2}{9}$ of a loaf of bread.

Hannah eats $\frac{5}{12}$ of the same loaf of bread.

How much of the loaf of bread is left?

2 marks

6 Calculate the following.

Give your answer as an improper fraction in its simplest form.

$$3\frac{1}{6} + 1\frac{3}{10} - \frac{17}{15}$$

2 marks

7 The Williams family uses $\frac{7}{10}$ of a pint of milk at breakfast,
$\frac{3}{5}$ of a pint of milk at lunch and $\frac{1}{4}$ of a pint of milk in the evening.
The Kang family uses $1\frac{5}{8}$ pints of milk in a day.

Which family uses more milk in one day? Show your working.

3 marks

"I can add and subtract fractions
by finding a common denominator."

Dividing Fractions

1 Calculate:

$$\frac{1}{3} \div 8$$

$$\frac{1}{10} \div 7$$

2 marks

2 Emmanuel is decorating his room. He is going to paint $\frac{1}{2}$ of one wall.

He is going to divide the painted section into 6 equal sections and one of these sections will be painted green.

What fraction of the whole wall is he going to paint green?

1 mark

3 Work out the following calculations.
Give your answers in their simplest form.

$$\frac{8}{15} \div 4$$

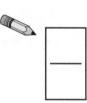

$$\frac{6}{7} \div 3$$

2 marks

4 Naomi has $\frac{6}{10}$ of a cheesecake.
She shares it equally between herself and her three sisters.

What fraction of the whole cheesecake does each girl get?
Give your answer in its simplest form.

1 mark

"I can divide fractions by whole numbers."

Equivalent Fractions and Decimals

1 Draw lines to join each fraction to its equivalent decimal.

$\frac{3}{10}$ 0.003

$\frac{3}{100}$ 0.3

$\frac{3}{1000}$ 0.03

1 mark

2 Fill in the boxes below with the missing fractions or decimals.

$0.007 = \boxed{}$ $\frac{19}{100} = \boxed{}$

$\frac{157}{1000} = \boxed{}$ $0.81 = \boxed{}$

2 marks

3 Convert the following fractions to decimals.

$\frac{4}{5} = \boxed{}$ $\frac{13}{20} = \boxed{}$

$\frac{4}{25} = \boxed{}$ $\frac{29}{500} = \boxed{}$

2 marks

4 Noah has 0.34 litres of hot chocolate in a flask.

What fraction of a litre of hot chocolate does he have?
Give your answer in its simplest form.

1 mark

Equivalent Fractions and Decimals

5 Write 0.48 as a fraction in its simplest form.

1 mark

6 Circle the decimal below that is equivalent to $\frac{5}{8}$.

0.125   0.4   0.625   0.58

1 mark

7 Look at the fraction $\frac{7}{8}$.

Work out the value of 7000 ÷ 8.

1 mark

Use the answer you've just found to write $\frac{7}{8}$ as a decimal.

1 mark

"I can convert fractions to decimals by dividing."

Fractions, Decimals and Percentages

1 Fill in the boxes with the missing fractions, decimals or percentages.

Give the fractions in their simplest form.

$$\frac{4}{5} \longrightarrow 0.8 \longrightarrow \boxed{}\%$$

1 mark

$$\frac{\boxed{}}{\boxed{}} \longrightarrow \boxed{} \longrightarrow 75\%$$

1 mark

$$\frac{\boxed{}}{\boxed{}} \longrightarrow 0.3 \longrightarrow \boxed{}\%$$

1 mark

2 Write **<**, **>** or **=** in each box to make the statement correct.

$$\frac{2}{5} \quad \boxed{} \quad 0.39$$

1 mark

$$0.05 \quad \boxed{} \quad \frac{3}{50}$$

1 mark

$$\frac{8}{25} \quad \boxed{} \quad 0.32$$

1 mark

3 Shoshanna and Leah are decorating some cakes. Shoshanna has decorated $\frac{7}{20}$ of the cakes. Leah has decorated 33% of the cakes.

Who has decorated more cakes? Show your working.

2 marks

SECTION THREE — FRACTIONS, DECIMALS & PERCENTAGES

Fractions, Decimals and Percentages

4 Put the values below in order from smallest to largest.

$$0.85 \qquad \frac{22}{25} \qquad 89\% \qquad \frac{43}{50}$$

smallest			largest

2 marks

5 Circle the three equivalent amounts listed below.

$$0.65 \qquad \frac{13}{20} \qquad 62\% \qquad \frac{39}{60}$$

$$13\% \qquad \frac{26}{50} \qquad 0.39 \qquad \frac{3}{5}$$

2 marks

6 On a long car journey, Mr Barlow has driven 27% of the distance and Mrs Barlow has driven $\frac{6}{25}$ of the distance.

Who has driven the greater distance? Show your working.

2 marks

How much of the journey is left? Give your answer as a percentage.

%

1 mark

"I can convert between fractions, decimals and percentages."

Ratio and Proportion

1 A bar of chocolate weighs 50 g.

How much will 7 bars of chocolate weigh?

g

1 mark

2 1 litre of orange paint costs £15.

How many litres of orange paint could you buy with £345?

litres

1 mark

3 A box of 4 muffins costs £3.60.

How much will 24 muffins cost?

£

1 mark

4 Joanna bought 6 sports drinks for £2.40.

How much does 1 sports drink cost?

£

1 mark

How much would 4 sports drinks cost?

£

1 mark

Ratio and Proportion

5 Use the shapes below to complete the following sentences.

The ratio of shaded to unshaded shapes is ☐ : ☐

1 mark

For every 2 triangles there are ☐ squares.

1 mark

6 A shop has a special offer on cans of lemonade.
For every 12 cans of lemonade you buy, you get a free glass.

How many free glasses will you get if you buy 48 cans of lemonade?

1 mark

How many cans of lemonade do you need to buy to get 11 free glasses?

1 mark

7 In a fish tank, for every 8 orange fish there are 3 blue fish.

There are 24 orange fish. How many blue fish are there?

1 mark

8 In a flock of sheep, 3 in every 7 sheep are female.
There are 27 female sheep in the flock.

What is the total number of sheep in the flock?

1 mark

Ratio and Proportion

9 The ratio of boys to girls in Year 5 is 6:7.
There are 42 boys in Year 5.

How many children are in Year 5?

10 Yusuf has a map of his town. 2 cm on the map represents 100 m
in real life. He draws a line on the map to show his journey to school.

The line Yusuf draws is 6 cm long.
How long is Yusuf's journey to school in real life?

m

1 mark

11 A recipe for tomato sauce uses the ingredients shown below.

Ingredients	
Tomatoes	600 g
Olive Oil	20 ml
Sugar	10 g

Henry uses 50 g of sugar.
How many grams of tomatoes will he need to use?

g

1 mark

Chloe uses 15 ml of olive oil.
How many grams of sugar will she need to use?

g

1 mark

"I can solve problems that are to do
with the relative sizes of two amounts."

Unequal Sharing

1 Ivan and Alex share a baguette in the ratio 1 : 4.

What fraction of the baguette does Ivan get?

1 mark

2 Fleur and Bridget share a bunch of grapes.
For every 3 grapes Fleur gets, Bridget gets 2.

There are 35 grapes in the bunch. How many does each girl get?

Fleur: ☐   Bridget: ☐

1 mark

3 Novak and Roger played tennis.
For every 4 points that Novak won, Roger won 3 points.

They played for a total of 63 points. How many did Roger win?

1 mark

4 Aki and Gemma are window cleaners. The ratio of windows
cleaned by Aki to windows cleaned by Gemma is 9 : 5.

Aki and Gemma are cleaning the windows of a school
which has 98 windows.
How many more windows does Aki clean than Gemma?

2 marks

Unequal Sharing

5 Andy, Jenny and Heather share £200 in the ratio 1 : 4 : 5.

Work out how much each person gets.

Andy: £

Jenny: £

Heather: £

6 All the chocolates in a box are either white or milk chocolate.
There are twice as many white chocolates as milk chocolates.

There are 42 chocolates in the box. How many are white chocolate?

7 A postman counted the number of letters and parcels he delivered one day.
For every 12 letters, he delivered 3 parcels. He delivered 55 items in total.

Complete the sentence below.

For every parcel the postman delivered, he delivered _____ letters.

How many parcels did he deliver that day?

Parcels:

How many letters did he deliver that day?

Letters:

"I can work out how to share things unequally."

Percentage Problems

1 Work out these percentages.

10% of 390 =

1% of 6800 =

1 mark

2 Calculate:

5% of 740

1 mark

15% of 2180

1 mark

3 In Applemouth Primary School there are 560 pupils. 35% of the pupils have blonde hair.

How many of the pupils have blonde hair?

1 mark

4 Larry buys a bike for £420 and sells it for 45% more than he paid for it.

How much money does Larry make when he sells the bike?

£

1 mark

Percentage Problems

(5) 35% of the books sold at a bookshop one week were comics. The percentages of the other types of books sold are shown in the table on the right.

Bookshop Sales	
Comics	35%
Novels	45%
Non-fiction	15%
Other	5%

The bookshop sold 860 books that week. How many comics did the bookshop sell?

1 mark

What was the total number of novels and non-fiction books sold?

1 mark

(6) Calculate 32% of 300.

1 mark

(7) Farmer Fairbank is selling duck eggs on his market stall.
On Saturday he has 400 duck eggs and sells 45% of them.
On Sunday he has 700 duck eggs and sells 58% of them.

What was the total number of duck eggs sold on Saturday and Sunday?

3 marks

SECTION FOUR — RATIO, PROPORTION & ALGEBRA

Percentage Problems

8 Calculate:

11 as a percentage of 25

[ ] %

1 mark

7 as a percentage of 20

[ ] %

1 mark

9 In a group of 15 friends, 9 of them like cheese.

What percentage of the group like cheese?

[ ] %

1 mark

10 In a bag of marbles, 7 are green, 20 are red and 8 are blue.

What percentage of the marbles are green?

[ ] %

1 mark

11 Sandeep has a fish tank with 20 fish in it.
He adds another 12 fish to the tank.

By what percentage has he increased the number of fish in the tank?

[ ] %

1 mark

Percentage Problems

(12) An antique mirror is bought for £2000 and sold for £3500.

What was the percentage profit?

[   ] %

2 marks

(13) Stuart and Miranda buy and sell old cars.
Stuart bought a car for £800 and sold it for a £160 profit.
Miranda bought a car for £250 and sold it for a £60 profit.

Who made the highest percentage profit? Show your working.

2 marks

(14) Two cereal brands are changing the amount of cereal in their boxes.
Nutios are changing from a 600 g box to a 750 g box.
Branpops are changing from a 300 g box to a 360 g box.

Which brand is increasing the amount of cereal by the biggest percentage?
Show your working.

2 marks

"I can find a percentage of an amount.
I can use percentages to compare amounts."

Similar Shapes

1 Enlarge shape A by a scale factor of 2.

Draw your answer on the grid below.

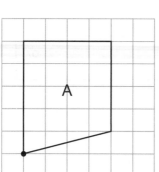

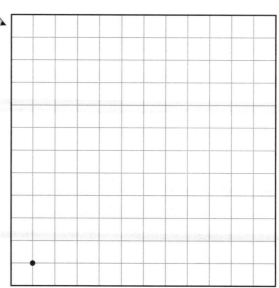

1 mark

2 Enlarge shape B by a scale factor of 3.

Draw your answer on the grid below.

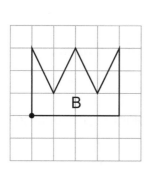

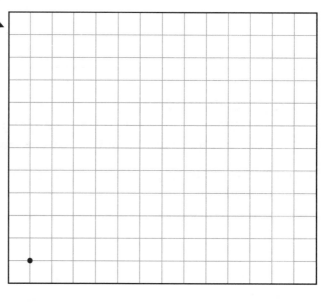

1 mark

3 A square with a side length of 14 cm is enlarged by a scale factor of 8.

What is the side length of the enlarged square?

cm

1 mark

Similar Shapes

4 A triangle is enlarged by a scale factor of 6.
The enlarged triangle has a height of 72 cm.

What was the height of the original triangle?

cm

5 Work out the scale factor for the enlargement from shape P to shape Q.

P

Q

6 Shape X is enlarge by a scale factor of 2 to give shape Y.
Shape Y is enlarged by a scale factor of 3 to give shape Z.

Draw and label shapes Y and Z on the grid below.

X

Work out the scale factor of the
enlargement from shape X to shape Z.

"I can enlarge a shape by a scale factor and
find the scale factor of an enlarged shape."

Section Four — Ratio, Proportion & Algebra

Formulas and Expressions

1 In a pack of hair slides there are 6 slides.

Complete this equation for the number of slides
in a given number of packs.

Number
of slides = [   ]

Complete this equation for the number of
packs given the number of slides.

Number
of packs = [   ]

2 Jasmine is buying cupcakes and doughnuts for her party.
Cupcakes cost 28p each and doughnuts cost 36p each.

Fill in the boxes to complete the formula for
the total cost (in pence) of the cupcakes and doughnuts.

Total
cost = [   ] × number of
cupcakes + 36 × [   ]

3 Habib is a chef. He makes pasta salad for a buffet.
He needs to cook 30 grams of pasta for each guest at the buffet.

Write a formula in words for the amount (in grams)
of pasta that Habib needs to cook for the buffet.

[Amount of pasta =   ]

How much pasta (in kilograms) will Habib need to cook for 120 guests?

[   ] kg

Formulas and Expressions

4 Vanessa is cooking a joint of beef. The cooking time (in minutes) is worked out using one of the formulas below.

To cook the beef rare:

$$\text{Time} = \frac{\text{Weight (grams)}}{20} + 15$$

To cook the beef well-done:

$$\text{Time} = \frac{\text{Weight (grams)}}{15} + 35$$

How long does Vanessa need to cook a 1500 g joint of beef if she wants it to be rare?

mins

1 mark

How much longer does she need to cook it if she wants it well-done instead of rare?

mins

1 mark

5 In a game, scoring a goal earns 5 points and scoring a penalty earns 3 points.

Write an expression for the total number of points scored by a team.

1 mark

A team scored 7 goals and 4 penalties. How many points did they get?

points

1 mark

"I can use formulas written in words."

Finding Missing Numbers 1

1 Use the equation y = 3x to answer these questions.

What is the value of y when x = 7?

y = [ ]

1 mark

What is the value of x when y = 36?

x = [ ]

1 mark

2 Find the values represented by △ and ☆.

11 × △ + 7 = 40

△ = [ ]

1 mark

35 ÷ 7 − ☆ = −1

☆ = [ ]

1 mark

3 Joe owns a music shop. On Monday he sells 22 guitar strings. On Tuesday he sells half as many, minus 3.

How many does he sell on Tuesday?

[ ]

1 mark

4 m is the number of DVDs that Elsa has. Brita has 8 times as many DVDs as Elsa. Dani has 6 fewer DVDs than Brita.

Write an expression to show the number of DVDs Dani has.

[ ]

1 mark

If Elsa has 9 DVDs, how many does Dani have?

[ ]

1 mark

"I can solve missing number problems using symbols and letters."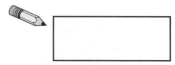

Finding Missing Numbers 2

1 Find all the possible pairs of positive whole-number values for ⬠ and ☆.

$$⬠ + 2☆ = 10$$

	⬠	☆
Pair 1		
Pair 2		
Pair 3		
Pair 4		

2 marks

2 Jeremiah writes down the following equation: $5M + N = 18$.

List three possible whole-number pairs of values for M and N.

	M	N
Pair 1		
Pair 2		
Pair 3		

2 marks

3 Angelo thinks of two numbers.

When he adds the two numbers, he gets 12.
When he multiplies the two numbers, he gets 27.
What are the two numbers that Angelo thought of?

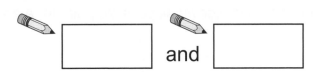

and

1 mark

4 The total number of mugs in a cupboard is given by $8A + 5B$.
A and B are positive whole numbers.

There are 44 mugs in the cupboard. Find the values of A and B.

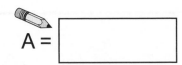 A = 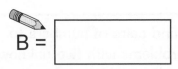 B =

1 mark

Finding Missing Numbers 2

5 Graham spends a total of £20 in a shop.
Baked beans (b) are £2 each. Bottles of ketchup (k) are £3 each.

He buys at least 1 of each item. List the three possible values of b and k.

2 marks

6 Laura is organising a birthday party.
She wants to invite twice as many girls (g) as boys (b).

Which of these equations must be true? Circle the correct answer.

$2g = b$ $\quad\quad$ $b - 2 = g$ $\quad\quad$ $2b = g$ $\quad\quad$ $b + 2 = g$

1 mark

7 Here are 7 cards. A, B and C stand for positive whole numbers.
They can represent the same number.

A $\quad$ C $\quad$ A $\quad$ B $\quad$ A $\quad$ B $\quad$ C

The sum of all the A and B cards is equal to the sum of the C cards.
If C = 11, write down all possible pairs for A and B.

2 marks

"I can find pairs of numbers to
solve problems with two unknowns,
and list all possible combinations."

Number Sequences

1 Write down the rules for these number sequences.

4, 11, 18, 25, 32...

> 1 mark

55, 49, 43, 37, 31...

> 1 mark

2 Write down the next three terms in each of these sequences.

3   14   25

...

> 1 mark

23   18   13

...

> 1 mark

3 Fill in the missing numbers in this sequence.

2   9

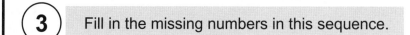

23   30

...

> 1 mark

4 Write down the missing terms in each of these two sequences.

−8   1   10

...

> 1 mark

−15   −23   −31...

> 1 mark

Number Sequences

5 A sequence starts 3, 7, 11, 15, 19...

What is the 10th term in the sequence?

1 mark

6 The rule for this sequence is "multiply by the same number each time".

Fill in the missing terms.

2   4   8   16  ...

1 mark

7 Write down the rules for the following sequences.

2, 20, 200, 2000...

1 mark

48, 24, 12, 6...

1 mark

8 The rule for the sequence below is "subtract the same number each time".

Fill in the missing terms.

6 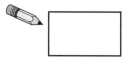 −2  −10...

2 marks

"I can make and describe number sequences."

Units and Conversions

1 For each of the following, circle the best estimate.

The length of a baked bean.

100 mm   1 cm   1 m   50 mm

The height of this book.

3 m   0.3 cm   60 cm   300 mm

The mass of a loaf of bread.

8 g   800 g   0.8 g   8 kg

The mass of a piece of A4 paper

5 g   100 g   0.5 kg   5 kg

2 marks

2 Maisie and Boris are packing for a camping trip.

Maisie packs 8.7 litres of water. How much is this in ml?

[   ] ml

1 mark

Boris packs 2500 g of rice. How much is this in kg?

[   ] kg

1 mark

3 Sophie's school is 500 m from her house.
She walks this distance ten times a week.

How many km is this in total?

[   ] km

1 mark

4 Fred was born a year and two weeks after Ava.
Neither of them was born in a leap year.

How many days after Ava was Fred born?

[   ] days

1 mark

Units and Conversions

5 A rubber ball weighs 2 ounces. How much would 10 rubber balls weigh?
Give your answer in pounds and ounces?

1 lb = 16 oz.

| lb | oz |

2 marks

6 Olaf keeps running around a track until he has
run 0.9 km in total. The track is 150 m long.

How many times does he run around the track?

1 mark

7 Caley has 3 toy cars. They measure 40 mm, 5.3 cm and 4.7 cm.
If she lines them up end-to-end, what would their total length be?

Give your answer in mm.

mm

1 mark

8 Imran has a 3-litre watering can which is full of water.
He pours half of it onto his flower bed.

How much water does Imran pour onto the flower bed?
Give your answer in ml.

ml

1 mark

Units and Conversions

9 At the beginning of the year Terrence weighed 72.4 kg.
At the end of the year he weighed 69.2 kg.

How many grams lighter was Terrence at the end of the year?

| g |

1 mark

10 In a TV advert break, there are four adverts which are each 15 seconds long, one that is 30 seconds long and one that is 45 seconds long.

How long is the advert break in minutes and seconds?

| minutes   seconds |

2 marks

11 Lucas is allowed to play computer games for 3 hours a week. On Monday he plays for 45 minutes and on Tuesday he plays for 22 minutes.

How many minutes does he have left for the rest of the week?

| minutes |

2 marks

12 Barry's car has enough petrol to travel 320 km.
Approximately how far is this in miles?

| miles |

1 mark

Units and Conversions

13 Kim follows the path shown on the map to the treasure at X.

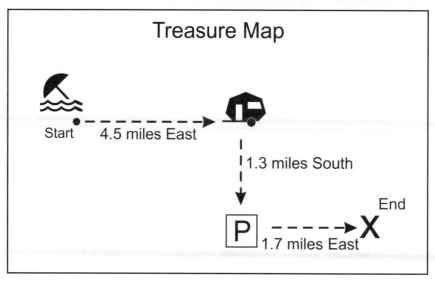

Treasure Map

Start — 4.5 miles East

1.3 miles South

P ----→X End
1.7 miles East

Approximately how many kilometres does Kim walk?

km

1 mark

The treasure contains gold coins. Each coin has a mass of 12 g.
Kim can carry a maximum of 24 kg.
What is the maximum number of coins she can carry?

2 marks

14 Whilst riding her bicycle, Mandy travels 18 km in an hour.

How many metres does she travel per minute?

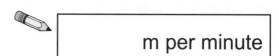

m per minute

2 marks

"I can convert between units of
length, mass, volume and time,
and between miles and kilometres."

Perimeters and Areas

1 Calculate the perimeter of these regular shapes.

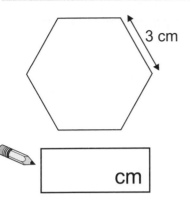

3 cm

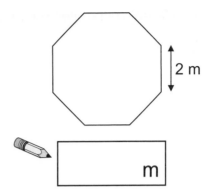

2 m

cm

m

2 The shape below is made up of five identical rectangles.

Work out the perimeter of the shape.

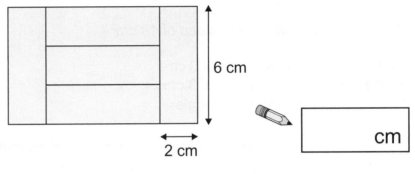

6 cm

2 cm

cm

What is the area of the shape?

cm²

3 Circle the shapes that have the same area.

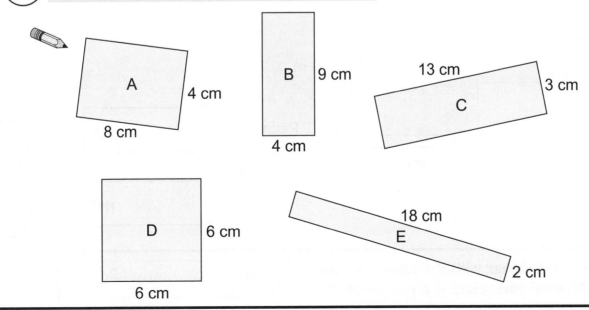

A

4 cm

8 cm

B 9 cm

4 cm

13 cm

C

3 cm

D 6 cm

6 cm

18 cm

E

2 cm

Perimeters and Areas

4 | Look at the grid below.

Draw two different rectangles on the grid, each with a perimeter of 10 cm.

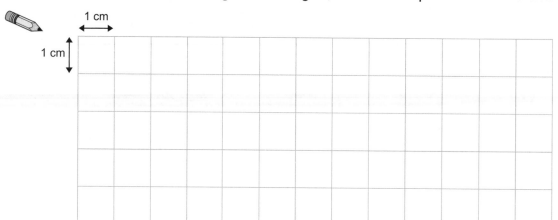

5 | Two different rectangles have areas of 18 cm².

Rectangle A has a side length of 9 cm.
Rectangle B has a side length of 3 cm.
Find the perimeter of each rectangle.

Rectangle A: Rectangle B:

cm   cm

6 | Calculate the perimeter and area of the shape below.

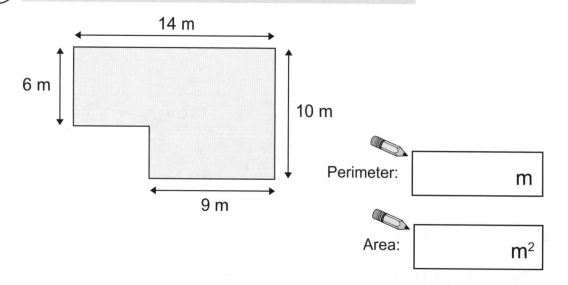

14 m

6 m

10 m

9 m

Perimeter: _____ m

Area: _____ m²

"I know that shapes with the same area can
have different perimeters and vice versa."

Areas of Triangles

1 Find the area of each triangle below.

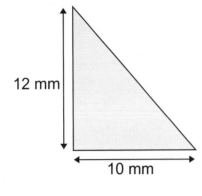

12 mm

10 mm

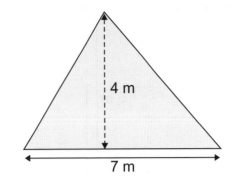

4 m

7 m

mm²

m²

2 The shape below is made from two triangles. Find its area.

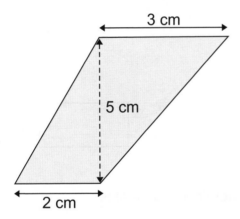

3 cm

5 cm

2 cm

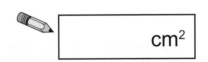
cm²

3 Ben is making a model pyramid for his project on Egypt.
It has four identical triangular faces and one square face.

Ben paints all of the faces yellow. What is the total area that he paints?

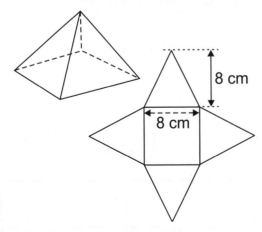

8 cm

8 cm

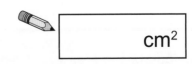
cm²

Areas of Triangles

4 The shape below is made up of a square and a triangle.

Find its area.

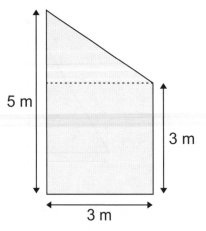

5 m

3 m

3 m

m²

2 marks

5 The diagonals of a square measure 12 cm.
By splitting the square into four triangles, find the area of the square.

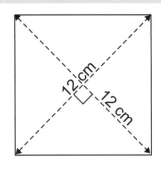

12 cm

12 cm

cm²

2 marks

6 A bathroom wall is decorated with 100 identical square tiles.

The picture to the right shows one of the tiles. Find the total grey area of the bathroom wall.

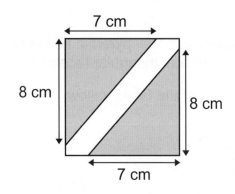

7 cm

8 cm

8 cm

7 cm

cm²

2 marks

"I can calculate the area of a triangle."

　　　　© **CGP** — NOT TO BE PHOTOCOPIED

Areas of Parallelograms

1   Find the area of each parallelogram below.

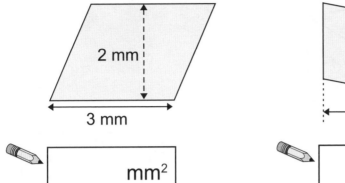

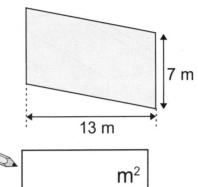

 mm²

 m²

2 marks

2   The shape below is made up of two parallelograms.

Find the total area of the shape.

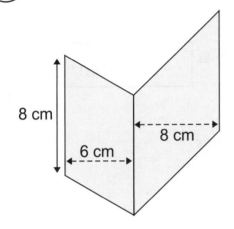

 cm²

2 marks

3   The white arrows on the rectangular road sign below are made from parallelograms.

Find the total area of the sign that is **not** white.

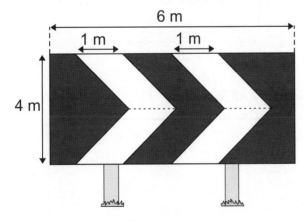

 m²

3 marks

"I can calculate the area of a parallelogram."

Volume

1 Find the volume of each cuboid below.

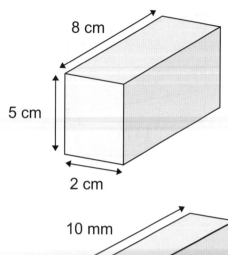

cm³

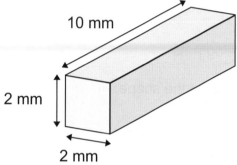

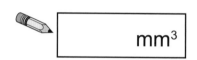

mm³

2 Mario's roof is leaking. He decides to put a plastic box under the leak to collect the water.

Mario has two plastic boxes.

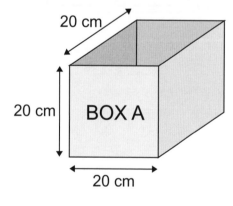

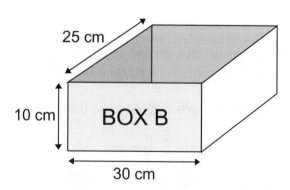

Which box will hold the most water? Show your working.

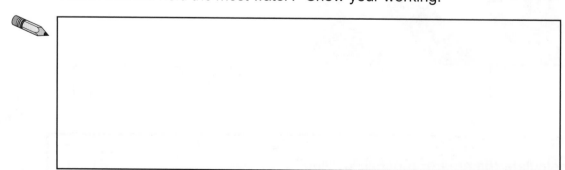

<u>Volume</u>

3 Shabina is making a cuboid-shaped swimming pool.
Her pool will be 20 m long and 5 m wide, with a depth of 2 m.

How many m³ of water will be in her pool when it is filled to the top?

m³

1 mark

4 The shape to the right is made up of cuboids.

Find its volume.

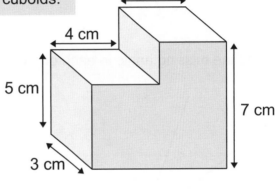

3 cm

4 cm

5 cm

7 cm

3 cm

cm³

2 marks

5 In a playground, a tunnel is made from a wooden cuboid, with a cuboid shaped hole all the way through.

Work out the volume of wood that makes up the tunnel.

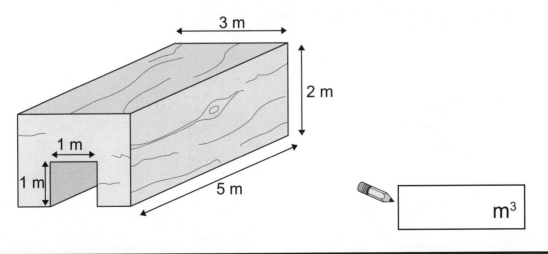

3 m

2 m

1 m

1 m

5 m

m³

2 marks

"I can calculate the volumes
of cubes and cuboids."

Angle Rules

1 Angle a = 103°.

Calculate the angles b, c and d.

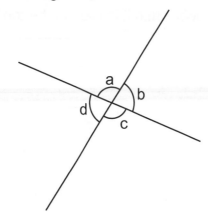

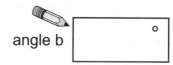
angle b

1 mark

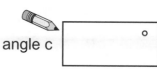
angle c

1 mark

angle d

°

1 mark

2 Find the missing angle in each of these diagrams.

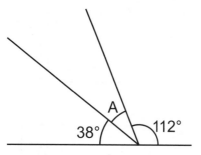

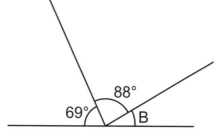

A =   °

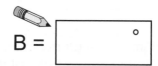
B =   °

2 marks

3 Find the missing angle in each of these diagrams.

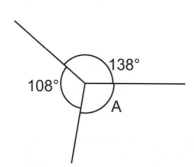

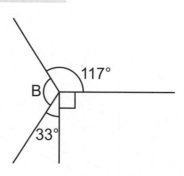

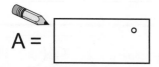
A =   °

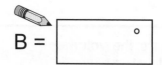
B =   °

2 marks

Angle Rules

4 There are five equal angles around a point.

Calculate the size of each angle.

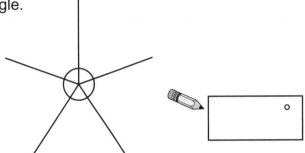

1 mark

5 Find the size of angle Q.

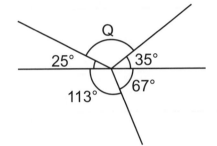

Q =

1 mark

6 Calculate the missing angles in the diagram below.

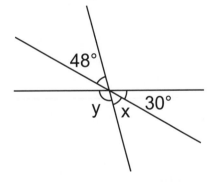

angle x

1 mark

angle y

1 mark

7 Calculate the angles A and B.

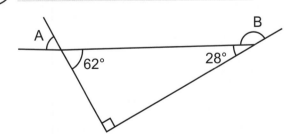

angle A

1 mark

angle B

1 mark

"I can use rules to find missing angles."

64

Drawing 2D Shapes

1 Using a ruler and a protractor or a set square, draw a square with sides of 4 cm.

1 mark

2 Using a ruler and a protractor or a set square, draw a 7 cm by 4 cm rectangle.

1 mark

3 Equilateral triangles have three equal angles.

Draw an equilateral triangle with sides of 3 cm.

1 mark

Drawing 2D Shapes

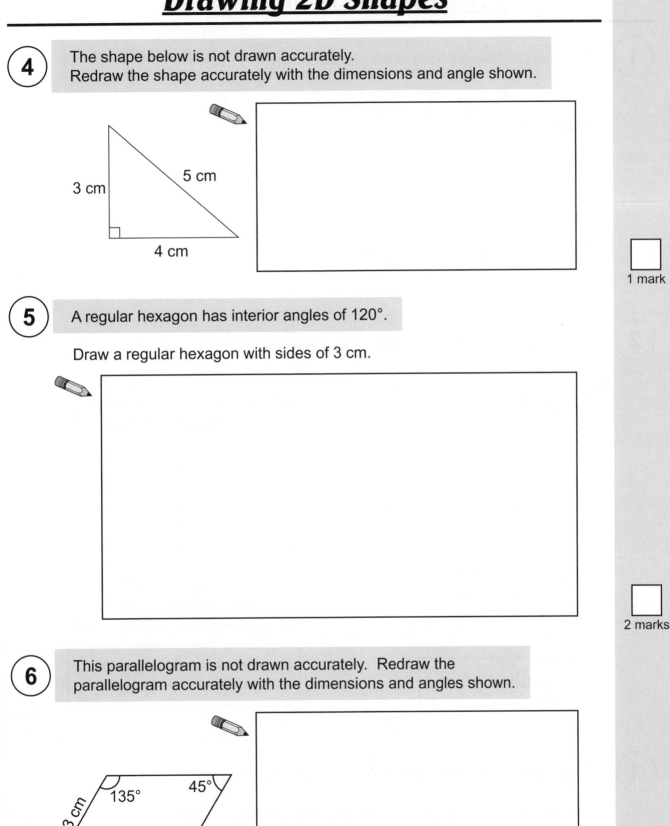

4 The shape below is not drawn accurately.
Redraw the shape accurately with the dimensions and angle shown.

5 cm

3 cm

4 cm

1 mark

5 A regular hexagon has interior angles of 120°.

Draw a regular hexagon with sides of 3 cm.

2 marks

6 This parallelogram is not drawn accurately. Redraw the parallelogram accurately with the dimensions and angles shown.

135°

45°

3 cm

45°

135°

6 cm

2 marks

"I can draw 2D shapes accurately."

SECTION SIX — GEOMETRY

Properties of Shapes

1 Complete the descriptions of the shapes below.

A square has ☐ right angles.

A trapezium has one pair of ☐ sides.

An equilateral triangle has three angles of ☐° .

2 Draw lines to match each shape to the correct description.

Rectangle

Kite

Rhombus

Parallelogram

4 equal-length sides and 2 pairs of equal angles.

2 pairs of equal-length sides and 2 pairs of equal angles.

2 pairs of equal-length sides and 4 equal angles.

2 pairs of equal-length sides and 1 pair of equal angles.

3 The distance around the outside edge of a circle is 20 cm.

Use one of the words below to complete the sentence.

radius   circumference   diameter

The ☐ of the circle is 20 cm.

Properties of Shapes

4 Draw a diameter on the circle below.
The centre of the circle is marked for you.

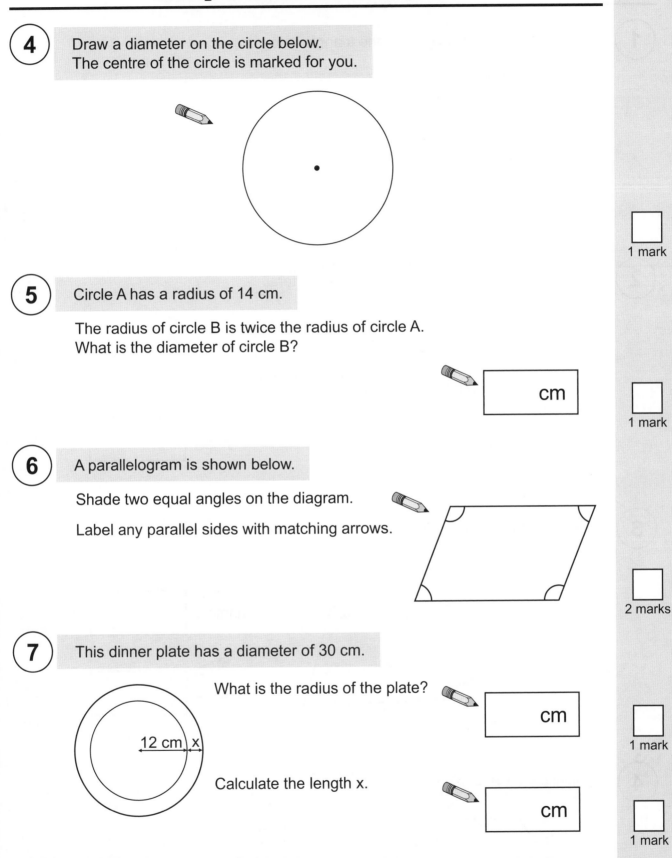

1 mark

5 Circle A has a radius of 14 cm.

The radius of circle B is twice the radius of circle A.
What is the diameter of circle B?

cm

1 mark

6 A parallelogram is shown below.

Shade two equal angles on the diagram.

Label any parallel sides with matching arrows.

2 marks

7 This dinner plate has a diameter of 30 cm.

What is the radius of the plate?

cm

1 mark

12 cm x

Calculate the length x.

cm

1 mark

"I know the properties of different shapes.
I can name the parts of a circle
and I know that the diameter of a
circle is twice the length of its radius."

SECTION SIX — GEOMETRY

Angles in Shapes

1 Calculate the size of angle x in the triangle below.

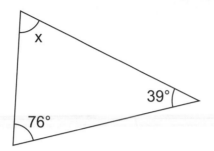

 x =

1 mark

2 Calculate the size of angle y in this quadrilateral.

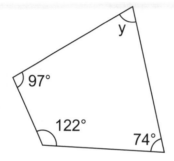

y =

1 mark

3 Calculate the size of angles a and b in this isosceles triangle.

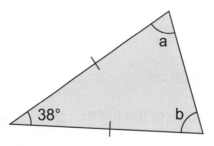

angle a

angle b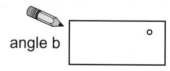

1 mark

4 Calculate the size of angle x in this rhombus.

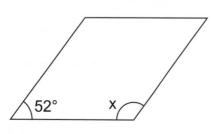

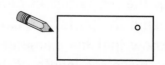

2 marks

Angles in Shapes

5 A nonagon is a nine-sided shape.

Calculate the size of the exterior angle of a regular nonagon.

°

1 mark

Calculate the size of the interior angle of a regular nonagon.

°

1 mark

6 An octagon is an eight-sided shape.

Work out the sum of the interior angles of a regular octagon.

°

1 mark

Work out the size of one interior angle of a regular octagon.

°

1 mark

7 This shape is an irregular pentagon.

x

146° 120°

63° 98°

What is the sum of the interior angles of this shape?

°

1 mark

Work out the size of angle x.

°

1 mark

"I can use what I know about shapes to find missing angles."

3D Shapes

1 Fill the gaps to complete the descriptions below.

 A cube has ⬚ faces.

The net of a square-based pyramid has ⬚ triangles

and one ⬚⬚⬚⬚ .

2 marks

2 For each net below, write down the name of the shape it makes.

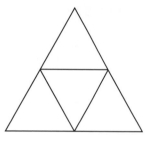   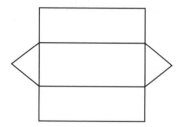

2 marks

3 The diagram below shows the same cuboid from 4 different angles.

Complete the net for the cuboid by drawing the symbols in the correct places.

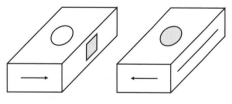
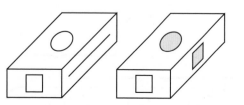

 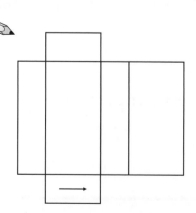

2 marks

3D Shapes

4 On the isometric grid below, draw the 3D shape the net makes.

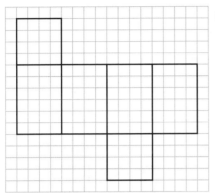 

1 mark

5 Look at the net below.

Circle the cube that could be made by this net.

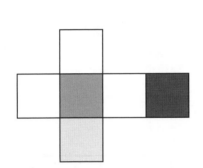 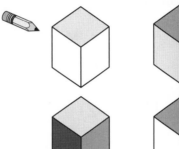 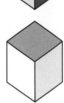

1 mark

6 Draw a net of the shape below on the grid.

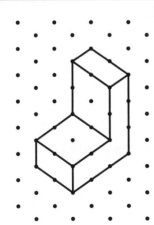 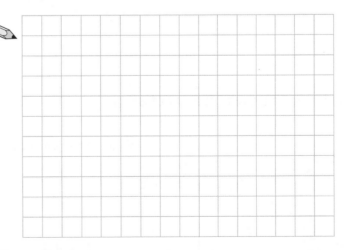

1 mark

"I can recognise and describe 3D shapes.
I can draw nets of 3D shapes.
I can use nets to draw 3D shapes accurately."

Coordinates

1 Write down the coordinates of the points plotted on the grid below.

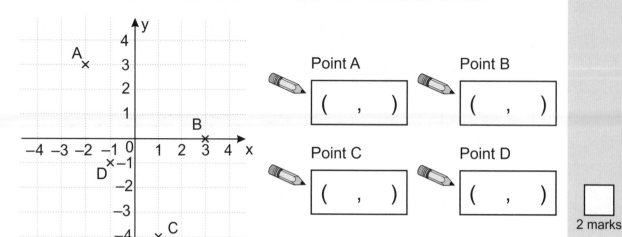

Point A

(,)

Point B

(,)

Point C

(,)

Point D

(,)

2 marks

2 Plot points E to J on the grid.

E (−3, 1) F (0, 4)

G (2, 0) H (4, −2)

I (−1, 0) J (−4, −1)

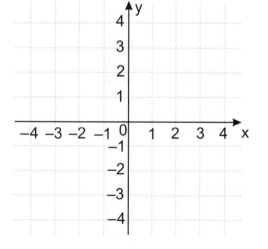

2 marks

3 A square is drawn on a set of axes.

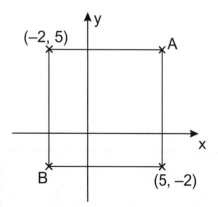

Find the coordinates of points A and B.

Point A

(,)

Point B

(,)

1 mark

Coordinates

4 Two identical rectangles are shown on the axes below.

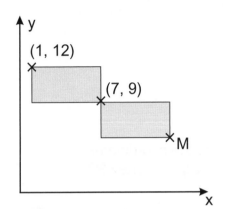

Work out the coordinates of point M.

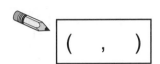

(,)

5 A regular pentagon is drawn on the set of axes below.

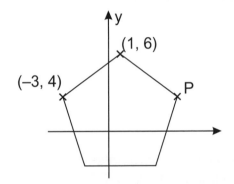

What are the coordinates of point P?

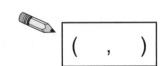

(,)

6 Two identical parallelograms are shown on the axes below.

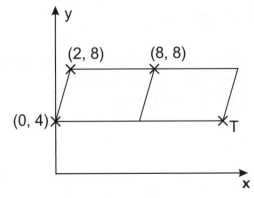

Find the coordinates of point T.

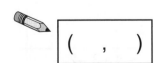

(,)

"I can use coordinates in four quadrants."

Section Six — Geometry

Reflection

1 Reflect shape A in the x-axis. Label the reflected shape B.

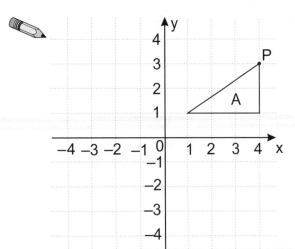

What are the coordinates of the image of vertex P?

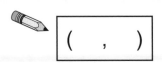

(,)

2 marks

2 Reflect shape C in the y-axis. Label the reflected shape D.

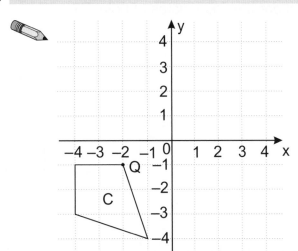

What are the coordinates of the image of vertex Q?

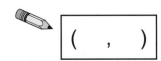

(,)

2 marks

3 Shape E has a vertex, R, with coordinates (3, −2).

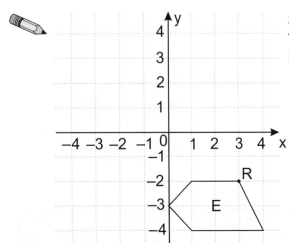

Shape E is reflected in one of the axes. The image of vertex R is (3, 2). Perform this reflection.

1 mark

Reflection

4 Shape F has a vertex, M, with coordinates (4, −1).

Shape F is reflected in the y-axis.
What are the coordinates of the image of M?

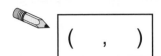

(,   )

1 mark

5 Reflect shape G in the x-axis. Label the reflected shape H.

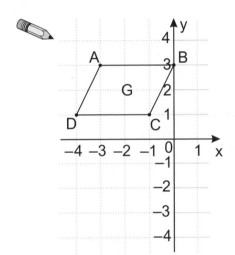

Write down the coordinates of the image of shape H.

Image of A

(,   )

Image of B

(,   )

Image of C

(,   )

Image of D

(,   )

2 marks

6 Shape J has a vertex, W, with coordinates (4, 1).

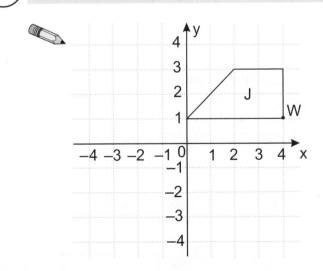

Reflect shape J in the x-axis.
Label this shape K.

1 mark

Reflect shape K in the y-axis.
Label this shape L.

1 mark

What are the coordinates of the image of vertex W on shape L?

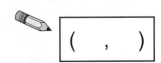

(,   )

1 mark

"I can reflect a shape in the axes of a grid and give the coordinates of the image."

Translation

1 Shape U is shown on the grid below.

Translate shape U 3 squares to the right and 4 squares down.
Label the translated shape V.

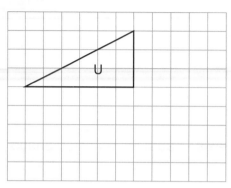

2 Shape X is shown on the grid below.

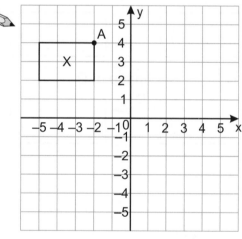

Translate shape X
+6 units horizontally
and −4 units vertically.
Label the translated shape Y.

What are the coordinates of the
translated vertex A on shape Y?

(,)

3 Shape K is shown on the grid below.

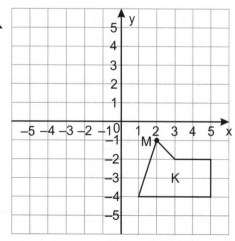

Translate shape K
−5 units horizontally
and +6 units vertically.
Label the translated shape L.

What are the coordinates of the
translated vertex M on shape L?

(,)

Translation

4 The coordinates of vertex Z on shape O are (–3, 2). Shape O is translated by –1 unit horizontally and +4 units vertically to give shape P.

Find the coordinates of the translated vertex Z on shape P.

(,)

1 mark

5 The coordinates of vertex J on shape N are (–4, –3). Shape N is translated, and the coordinates of the translated vertex J are (1, 1).

What translation was performed on shape N?

units horizontally

units vertically

1 mark

6 The coordinates of vertex P on shape T are (a, b). Shape T is translated so that the coordinates of the translated vertex P are (a – 6, b + 1).

Perform this translation.

1 mark

What are the coordinates of the translated vertex P?

(,)

1 mark

7 Vertex C on shape Y has the coordinates (a, b) = (–2, 4). Shape Y is translated so that the coordinates of the translated vertex C are (a + 1, b + 2).

Find the coordinates of the translated vertex C.

(,)

1 mark

"I can translate shapes using coordinates."

Line Graphs

1   Ava has two pet hamsters called Billy and Fred.
She weighs each hamster every month.

She records their masses in a table.

Billy's mass at 2 months is missing from the table.
Use the graph below to fill in the table.

Age (months)	1	2	3	4	5
Billy's mass (g)	40		80	78	88
Fred's mass (g)	40	60	70	75	75

Use the information in the table to plot Fred's mass on the line graph.

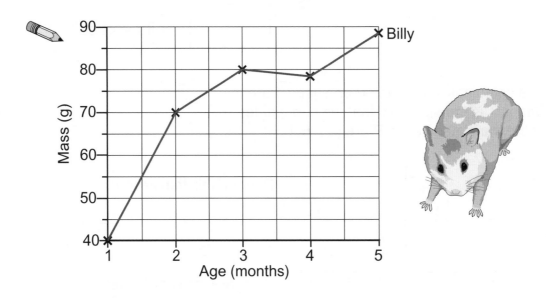

Estimate the mass of Billy at
two and a half months old.

_____ g

Billy was ill for a few weeks and didn't eat properly.
When do you think this was? Tick the correct box.

☐ Between 1 and 2 months.	☐ Between 3 and 4 months.
☐ Between 2 and 3 months.	☐ Between 4 and 5 months.

Line Graphs

2 This graph converts between British pounds (£) and American dollars ($).

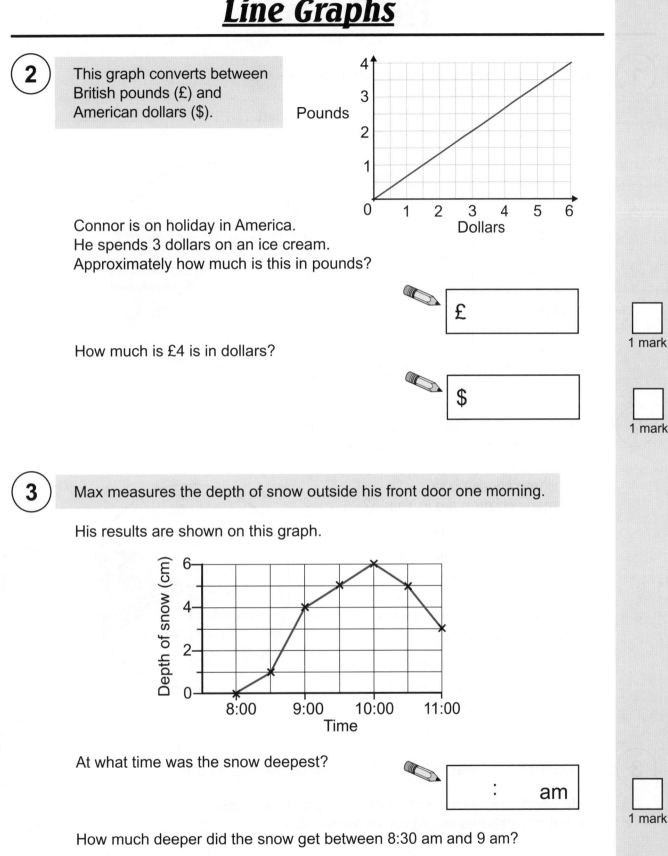

Pounds

Connor is on holiday in America.
He spends 3 dollars on an ice cream.
Approximately how much is this in pounds?

£ [   ]

1 mark

How much is £4 is in dollars?

$ [   ]

1 mark

3 Max measures the depth of snow outside his front door one morning.

His results are shown on this graph.

At what time was the snow deepest?

[:   ] am

1 mark

How much deeper did the snow get between 8:30 am and 9 am?

[   ] cm

1 mark

"I can read and draw line graphs."

SECTION SEVEN — STATISTICS

Pie Charts

1 48 children vote on where they should go for a trip.

The results of the vote are shown in the pie chart.
Use the pie chart to complete the table of results.

Trip destination	Number of votes
Zoo	
Funfair	
Waterpark	
Beach	

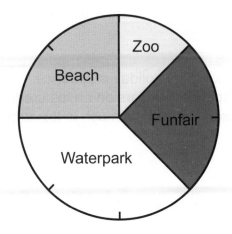

2 marks

2 The school lunch choices of the children in Year 6 are shown in the pie chart below.

20 children chose pizza.
How many children are in Year 6?

 children

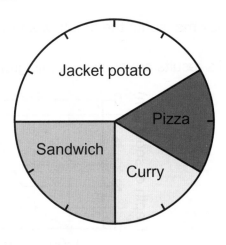

1 mark

How many more children chose a sandwich than curry?

 children

1 mark

3 10 children in a Healthy Eating Club have dressed up as fruit.

Kyle wants to draw a pie chart of their costume choices.
How many degrees will represent each child?

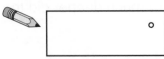 °

1 mark

2 children dressed as bananas.
How many degrees are needed for this sector?

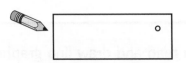 °

1 mark

Pie Charts

4 The table shows the favourite superheroes of 60 children.

Work out the angle for each superhero and use it to draw a pie chart.

Superhero	Number of children	Angle
Turnip Man	15	
Thunder Smash	30	
Magic Mary	10	
Bolt Girl	5	

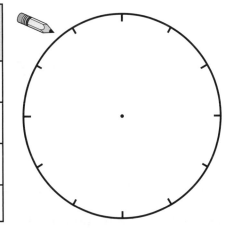

2 marks

5 Holly recorded the number of each type of bird that visited her garden one day. She counted 120 birds in total.

Her results are shown in this pie chart.

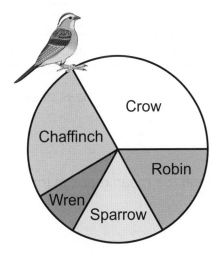

How many sparrows and wrens did she see? Measure the angles with a protractor.

Sparrows    Wrens

1 mark

Holly has made a mistake. Four of the birds she thought were crows were actually jackdaws, so her pie chart is wrong.

What size should the jackdaw sector be?

 °

1 mark

"I can draw and read pie charts."

SECTION SEVEN — STATISTICS

The Mean

1 Find the mean of each set of numbers.

8, 4, 5, 7

1 mark

3, 12, 11, 5, 20, 15

1 mark

2 Lydia weighs the eggs that her hen lays over five days.

Their masses are recorded in this table.

Day	Mon	Tue	Wed	Thur	Fri
Mass (g)	40	55	50	60	45

What is the total mass of all the eggs?

g

1 mark

Find the mean mass of the eggs.

g

1 mark

3 The number of photos Diego took on each day of his holiday is shown in this bar graph.

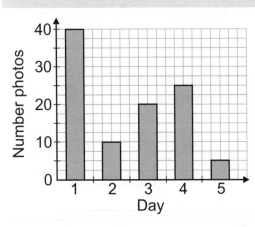

What is the mean number of photos he took each day?

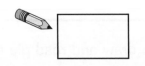

1 mark

The Mean

4 A shop sells four types of cake. The prices are listed below.

55p, £1.25, 90p, £1.10

Find the mean price in pence.

| p |

The shop starts selling an extra type of cake.
The mean price of cake in the shop does not change.
How much is the new type of cake?

| p |

1 mark

5 A packet of bacon says that the average content is 5 slices.

Maria counts the number of slices of bacon in 20 packets and records the data in a table.

Number of slices	3	4	5	6
Number of packets with this many slices	8	5	6	1

What is the total number of slices in the 20 packets?

1 mark

Is the claim on the packet of bacon correct? Explain your answer.

2 marks

6 Six pupils took a spelling test. Five of their marks are shown below.

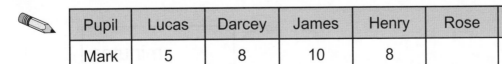

Pupil	Lucas	Darcey	James	Henry	Rose	Sarah
Mark	5	8	10	8		7

2 marks

The mean mark is 7. Work out Rose's mark and fill in the table.

"I know what the mean is.
I can calculate and use the mean."

Practice Test 2

1   Calculate 4686 ÷ 22.

1 mark

2   Write the following numbers in order starting with the **smallest**.

1.407   1.7   1. 074   1.705   1.450

smallest   largest

1 mark

3   Stephanie's office is 17 km away from her home. She drives from her home to her office. Here is a line graph of her journey.

On the way Stephanie stops twice to pick up friends.
How much time does she spend waiting for her friends?

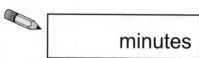 minutes

1 mark

Stephanie begins her journey at 7:15 am.
What time does she arrive at her office?

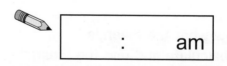   :   am

1 mark

4 What is the biggest common factor of 12, 18 and 30?

1 mark

5 What area of the rectangle is shaded below?

12 cm

7 cm

3 cm

cm²

2 marks

6 Sarah started practising for a sponsored walk on Monday.
On Tuesday she walked double the distance she had walked on Monday.
On Wednesday she walked 3 times as far as she walked on Monday.
By Wednesday evening she had walked a total of 30.6 km.

How far did she walk on Monday? Show your working.

km

2 marks

7 The temperature inside an attic was monitored over 24 hours.
At 2 am the temperature was –3 °C. By 3 pm it had risen by 12 °C.

What was the temperature inside the attic at 3 pm?

°C

1 mark

8 Complete this table. Give all fractions in their simplest form.

Fraction	Decimal	Percentage
	0.09	
		80%
$\frac{3}{8}$		

2 marks

9 Here is a parallelogram.

Calculate the shaded angles a, b and c.

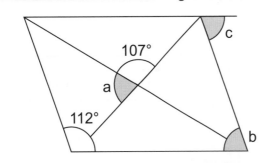

 a = [   ]°   b = [   ]°   c = [   ]°

2 marks

10 A factory produces packs of bird seed. Each pack contains 1.2 kg of seed. The factory packs up a total of 600 kg of seed each day.

How many packs does the factory produce each day?

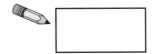

1 mark

The factory sells each pack of bird seed for £2.35.
A pet shop buys 48 packs.

How much did the pet shop pay?

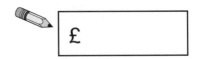 £ [   ]

1 mark

11 Parallelogram ABCD is drawn on the grid below.

Draw its reflection in the x-axis.

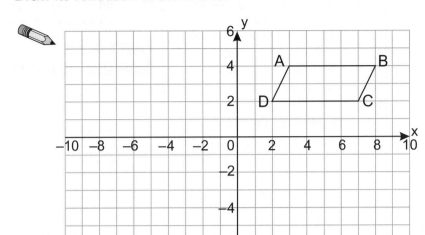

1 mark

12 The number of snails removed from the school greenhouse each week for several weeks is shown below.

$$6, \ 9, \ 11, \ 10, \ 7, \ 8, \ 9, \ 4$$

What is the mean number of snails collected each week?

1 mark

13 Calculate the following.

$$\frac{2}{7} \times \frac{3}{5}$$

$$\frac{2}{3} \div 3$$

1 mark

14 What is the value of k when 3k + 14 = 32?

k =

1 mark

Total

Answers

Test 1 — Pages 2-5

Q1 **540 300, 504 030, 54 300, 53 400** *(1 mark)*

Q2 **47 350, 47 300, 47 000**
(2 marks for all three correct. Otherwise 1 mark for any two correct.)

Q3
$$\begin{array}{r} 6\ 7\ 5 \\ \times\quad 3\ 8 \\ \hline 5\ 4\,_6 0\,_4 0 \\ 2\ 0\,_2 2\,_1 5\ 0 \\ \hline \mathbf{2\ 5\ 6\ 5\ 0} \end{array}$$ *(1 mark)*

Q4 $12 = 3 \times 4$, so multiply the numerator by 4.
$2 \times 4 = 8$, so $\frac{2}{3} = \mathbf{\frac{8}{12}}$
Working from the right-hand fraction to the left:
$1 \times 8 = 8$, so multiply the right-hand denominator by 8.
$2 \times 8 = 16$, so $\frac{8}{\mathbf{16}} = \frac{1}{2}$
(1 mark for both correct.)
$\frac{3}{4} + \frac{2}{3} = \frac{9}{12} + \frac{8}{12}$
$= \frac{17}{12} = \mathbf{1\frac{5}{12}}$ *(1 mark)*

Q5
$$12\ \overline{)\ 1\ ^1 8\ ^6 5}\quad \begin{array}{c}1\ 5\ \text{r}\ 5\end{array}$$
So the couple must buy **16** packs *(1 mark)*.

Q6 Angles at a point = 360°
so angle x = 360° ÷ 5 = **72°**
(1 mark)

The triangles are isosceles, so angle y and the unmarked angle are equal.
Angles in a triangle = 180°
So y + y + 72° = 180°
2y = 180° − 72° = 108°
y = 108° ÷ 2 = **54°** *(1 mark)*

Q7 There are 1½ lots of 16 biscuits in 24 biscuits.
So she'll need 1½ lots of 22 squares of chocolate
= 1 × 22 + ½ × 22
= 22 + 11 = **33** squares
(1 mark)

Q8 Height = 6 × 3 = **18 cm**
Base = 4 × 3 = **12 cm**
(1 mark for both correct)

Q9 40 ÷ 5 = 8, 8 × 8 = 64 km
64 × 5 = **320 km**
(2 marks for correct answer. Otherwise 1 mark for correct working.)

Q10 Volume = l × w × h
= 12 × 9 × 5
= **540 cm³** *(1 mark)*

Q11 The shape moves 4 units along to the right and 6 units up the y-axis. So the new coordinates of P are
(1 + 4 , 6 + 6) = **(5, 12)**
(1 mark)

Q12 10% of £290 = £29
20% of £240 = 2 × 29 = £58
Sale price = 290 − 58
= **£232** *(2 marks for correct answer. Otherwise 1 mark for calculating 20% correctly.)*

Q13 f = 6 and s = 9, so
E = (7 × 6) + (4 × 9)
= 42 + 36 = **£78**
(1 mark)

Q14
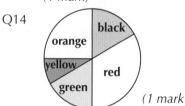
(1 mark

The 'green' sector of the pie chart measures 60°.
$\frac{60}{360} = \frac{1}{6}$, so number of green sweets = 24 ÷ 6 = **4**
(1 mark)

Section One — Number & Place Value

Pages 6-7 — Ordering Numbers

Q1 **£8 463 700** *(1 mark)*

Q2 **Twenty eight million, seven hundred and forty thousand, eight hundred and twenty seven.** *(1 mark)*

Q3 **7 000 000**
and **50 000** *(1 mark)*

Q4 **Redland** *(1 mark)*

Q5 **70 000** *(1 mark)*

Q6 **15 024 888, 15 024 764, 15 023 223, 15 023 096**
(1 mark)

Q7 **98 875 433** *(1 mark)*
33 457 898 *(1 mark)*

Pages 8-9 — Negative Numbers

Q1 5 − 8 = **−3**
−3 + 12 = **9** *(1 mark)*

Q2 To get each term of the sequence, you subtract 15 from the previous term.
5 − 15 = **−10**
−10 − 15 = **−25** *(1 mark)*

Q3 −2 + 18 = **16** *(1 mark)*

Q4 −5 − **13** = −18
−12 + 9 = −3 *(1 mark)*

Q5 Work out the places to 0, then the places after 0.
−6 + 6 = 0
0 + 11 = 11
6 + 11 = **17 °C** *(1 mark)*

Q6 It takes £88 to get to £0:
−£88 + £88 = £0
That leaves
£150 − £88 = £62
So −£88 + £150 = **£62**
(1 mark)
Work out the places to 0, then the places after 0.
−28 + 28 = 0
0 + 32 = 32
28 + 32 = **£60** *(1 mark)*

Q7 −8 + 3 = −5
−17 = −10 − 7 *(1 mark)*

Q8 −50 − 18 = **−68**
−14 + 18 = **4**
(1 mark for both correct.)

Pages 10-11 — Rounding

Q1 **25 500** and **509 000**
(1 mark)

Q2 78 705 rounded to the nearest **hundred** is 78 700.
(1 mark)
987 537 rounded to the nearest **ten thousand** is 990 000. *(1 mark)*

Q3 9000 + 7000 = **16 000**
(1 mark)

Q4 **18 000 000**
29 000 000 *(1 mark)*

Q5 **3.55** *(1 mark)*

Q6 **25.5** and **50.0** *(1 mark)*

Answers

Q7 $50 + 40 + 30 =$ **120 seconds**
(2 marks for the correct answer. Otherwise 1 mark for rounding the times correctly.)

Q8 $15.7 + 23.1 =$ **38.8 grams**
(2 marks for the correct answer. Otherwise 1 mark for rounding the weights correctly.)

Section Two — Calculations

Pages 12-13 — Written Multiplication

Q1 $20 \times 1500 =$ **30 000**
(1 mark)

Q2
```
      2 7
×     1 5
  1 3₃ 5
  2 7 0
  4₁ 0 5  (1 mark)
```

Q3
```
      3 7 4
×       2 3
  1 1₂ 2₁ 2
  7₁ 4 8 0
  8 6₁ 0 2
```
(2 marks for the correct answer. Otherwise 1 mark for working using long multiplication with no more than one error.)

Q4
```
      3 6 5
×       1 6
  2 1₃ 9₃ 0
  3 6 5 0
  5 8₁ 4 0  grams
```
(2 marks for the correct answer. Otherwise 1 mark for working using long multiplication with no more than one error.)

Q5
```
      1 6 9
×       2 4
    6₂ 7₃ 6
  3₁ 3₁ 8 0
  4₁ 0₁ 5 6  (1 mark)
```

```
      8 7
×     1 5
  4 3₃ 5
  8 7 0
  1 3₁ 0 5  (1 mark)
```

Q6
```
      4 7 2 3
×         6 1
  4 7 2 3
  2 8₄ 3₁ 3₁ 8 0
  2 8 8₁ 1₁ 0 3
```
(2 marks for the correct answer. Otherwise 1 mark for working using long multiplication with no more than one error.)
```
      3 8 1 6
×         4 4
  1 5₃ 2 6₂ 4
  1 5₃ 2 6₂ 4 0
  1 6 7 9₁ 0 4
```
(2 marks for the correct answer. Otherwise 1 mark for working using long multiplication with no more than one error.)

Q7 $2589 \times 20 = 51\ 780$
(1 mark)
$750 \times 42 = 31\ 500$ *(1 mark)*
$51\ 780 + 31\ 500$
$=$ **83 280 km** *(1 mark)*

Pages 14-15 — Written Division

Q1 **486** should be circled
(1 mark)
Sample working:
```
      4 8 6
9 ) 4 ⁴3 ⁷7 ⁵4
```

Q2 $756 \div 12 =$ **63** *(1 mark)*
Sample working:
```
      6 3
12 ) 7 ⁷5 ³6
```

Q3
```
       6 8
11 ) 7 ⁷4 ⁸8  (1 mark)
```
```
      6 9 4
8 ) 5 ⁵5 ⁵7 ³2  (1 mark)
```

Q4 $6384 \div 21 =$ **304**
```
         3 0 4
21 ) 6 3 8 4
   − 6 3
       0 8 4
   −     8 4
           0
```
(2 marks for the correct answer. Otherwise 1 mark for long division with no more than one error.)

Q5 $4404 \div 12 =$ **367**
```
          3 6 7
12 ) 4 ⁴4 ⁸0 ⁸4
```
(2 marks for the correct answer. Otherwise 1 mark for long division with no more than one error.)

Q6 Sample working:
```
          2 7 r 3
15 ) 4 0 8
   − 3 0
       1 0 8
     − 1 0 5
           3
```
So she can make **27** bracelets *(1 mark)*. She will have **3 cm** left over *(1 mark)*.

Q7 The remainder is **2**.
```
          3 4 5 r 2
22 ) 7 5 9 2
   − 6 6
       9 9
     − 8 8
         1 1 2
       − 1 1 0
             2
```
(2 marks for the correct answer. Otherwise 1 mark for long division with no more than one error.)

Q8 The teacher will get **14** sweets.
```
          1 3 2 r 14
29 ) 3 8 4 2
   − 2 9
       9 4
     − 8 7
         7 2
       − 5 8
         1 4
```
(2 marks for the correct answer. Otherwise 1 mark for long division with no more than one error.)

Pages 16-17 — Multiplying and Dividing with Decimals

Q1
6.82×1000 —— 6820
$6.82 \div 10$ — 0.0682
6.82×100 — 682
$6.82 \div 100$ — 0.682
(1 mark for all lines drawn correctly)

Answers

Q2 $4 \times 12 = 48$
4 is 10 times larger than 0.4,
so divide by 10.
$48 \div 10 = \textbf{4.8}$ *(1 mark)*

$81 \div 9 = 9$
81 is 10 times larger than 8.1,
so divide by 10.
$9 \div 10 = \textbf{0.9}$ *(1 mark)*

Q3

```
      3 8
  ×     7
  2 6₅6
```

38 is 10 times larger than
3.80, so divide by 10.
$£266 \div 10 = \textbf{£26.60}$
(1 mark)

Q4

```
      1 6 8
  ×       8
  1 3₅4₆4
```

168 is 100 times larger than
1.68, so divide by 100.
$1344 \text{ m} \div 100 = \textbf{13.44 m}$
(1 mark)

Q5

```
      3 7 4
7 ) 2 ²6 ⁵1 ²8
```

2618 is 10 times larger than
261.8, so divide by 10.
$374 \div 10 = \textbf{37.4 litres}$
(1 mark)

Q6

```
          4 2 4
14 ) 5 9 3 6
   − 5 6
       3 3
     − 2 8
         5 6
       − 5 6
             0
```

5936 is 100 times larger than
59.36, so divide by 100.
$424 \div 100 = \textbf{4.24}$ *(1 mark)*

Q7

```
      1 6 8 4
  ×         5
  8₃4₄2₂0
```

1684 is 100 times larger than
16.84, so divide by 100.
$8420 \div 100 = \textbf{84.2 miles}$
(1 mark)

15 minutes is quarter of
one hour so divide by 4.

```
      4 2 1
4 ) 1 ¹6 8 4
```

1684 is 100 times larger than
16.84, so divide by 100.
$421 \div 100 = \textbf{4.21 miles}$
(1 mark)

Pages 18-19 — Order of Operations

Q1   **26** and **10** *(1 mark)*

Q2   **8 + 2 × 8** and **(7 + 5) × 2** = 24
9 ÷ 3 − 6 and **9 − 3 × 4** = −3
8 + 8 ÷ 4 and **(5 × 6) ÷ 3** = 10
(2 marks for all three pairs correct. Otherwise 1 mark for linking one pair correctly.)

Q3 $6 \times 14 \div 21 = \textbf{4}$
(2 marks for the correct answer. Otherwise 1 mark for calculating the total number of biscuits as 84.)

Q4 $2 \times 3 = 6$ packets a day
$6 \times 7 = 42$ packets a week
$42 \div 5 = 8 \text{ r } 2$
So she will need **9 boxes**.
(2 marks for the correct answer. Otherwise 1 mark for calculating the number of packets used each week.)

Q5   Work out how much a
sausage roll costs:
$£32.24 \div 26 = £1.24$
Find the cost of 17 sausage
rolls: $£1.24 \times 17 = \textbf{£21.08}$
(2 marks for the correct answer. Otherwise 1 mark for calculating the price of one sausage roll.)

Q6   The cost of one of each item:
$24p + 70p + 35p = £1.29$
Cost of six of each:
$£1.29 \times 6 = £7.74$
Change from £10:
$£10 − £7.74 = \textbf{£2.26}$
(2 marks for the correct answer. Otherwise 1 mark for some correct working.)

Q7 $12 \times 19p = 228p$
$£5 = 500p$
$500p − 228p = 272p$
$272 \div 22 = 12 \text{ r } 8$
So she could buy **12 apples**.
(2 marks for the correct answer. Otherwise 1 mark for finding the amount spent on yoghurts.)

Page 20 — Estimation and Accuracy

Q1   You'd estimate the answer to
be about $800 \div 40 = 20$,
so **21.1** should be circled.
(1 mark)

Q2 $(300 \times 20) \div 6$
$= 6000 \div 6 = \textbf{1000}$ *(1 mark)*

Q3   33.549 is between 30 and 36.
$30 \div 6 = 5$ and $36 \div 6 = 6$
So $33.549 \div 6$ is
between 5 and 6. *(1 mark)*

Q4   Estimate the calculation:
$(10 \times 25) − 10 = 240$
So she is not correct.
(1 mark)

Pages 21-22 — Factors, Multiples and Primes

Q1   **1, 2, 3, 4, 6, 8, 9, 12, 18, 24, 36, 72** *(1 mark)*

Q2   **24, 48** and **72** should be
circled. *(1 mark)*

Q3   **41, 43, 47**
(2 marks for the correct answers. Otherwise 1 mark for two correct numbers.)

Q4   Factors of 36:
1, 2, 3, 4, 6, 9, 12, 18, 36
Factors of 54:
1, 2, 3, 6, 9, 18, 27, 54
Common factors:
1, 2, 3, 6, 9, 18
(2 marks for all six correct common factors. Otherwise 1 mark for finding all the factors of 36 or of 54.)

Q5 $3 \times 5 \times 7 = \textbf{105}$ *(1 mark)*

Q6   Multiples of 6:
6, 12, 18, 24, 30, 36, 42, 48
Multiples of 9:
9, 18, 27, 36, 45
So the common multiples are
18 and **36** *(1 mark)*.

Q7   Factors of 52: 1, 2, 4, 13, 26,
52. So Geoff could be
thinking of **2** or **13**.
(2 marks for both correct values. Otherwise 1 mark for one correct value.)

Q8   **Factors of 28:**
1, 2, 4, 7, 14, 28
1 + 2 + 4 + 7 + 14 = 28
So, 28 is a perfect number.
(1 mark)

Q9   Sample answer: **2 + 3 = 5**
(1 mark for adding 2 to any other prime number.)

Answers

Section Three — Fractions, Decimals & Percentages

Page 23 — Fractions

Q1 $\frac{6}{9}$ and $\frac{8}{12}$ should be circled
(1 mark)

Q2 $\frac{5}{8} = \frac{40}{\mathbf{64}}$, $\frac{4}{7} = \frac{\mathbf{12}}{21}$, $\frac{2}{5} = \frac{18}{45}$
(2 marks for all three correct, otherwise 1 mark for two correct.)

Q3 $\frac{12}{66} = \frac{\mathbf{2}}{\mathbf{11}}$, $\frac{36}{96} = \frac{\mathbf{3}}{\mathbf{8}}$, $\frac{121}{88} = \frac{\mathbf{11}}{\mathbf{8}}$
(2 marks for all three correct, otherwise 1 mark for two correct.)

Q4 Pippa has shaded $\frac{9}{20}$ squares.
$\frac{9}{20} = \frac{45}{100}$ so Kai needs to shade **45** squares *(1 mark)*

Q5 E.g. 36 is a common multiple of 9 and 12.
$\frac{8}{9} = \frac{8 \times 4}{9 \times 4} = \frac{\mathbf{24}}{\mathbf{36}}$ *(1 mark)*.
$\frac{13}{12} = \frac{13 \times 3}{12 \times 3} = \frac{\mathbf{39}}{\mathbf{36}}$ *(1 mark)*.

Page 24 — Comparing Fractions

Q1 Make equivalent fractions with the same denominator:
$\frac{4}{3} = \frac{24}{18}$, $\frac{5}{6} = \frac{15}{18}$, $\frac{10}{9} = \frac{20}{18}$
and $\frac{17}{18}$. So the order is:
$\frac{\mathbf{5}}{\mathbf{6}}, \frac{\mathbf{17}}{\mathbf{18}}, \frac{\mathbf{10}}{\mathbf{9}}, \frac{\mathbf{4}}{\mathbf{3}}$ *(1 mark)*

Q2 Make equivalent fractions with the same denominator:
$\frac{3}{4} = \frac{27}{36}$, $\frac{8}{9} = \frac{32}{36}$, $\frac{5}{6} = \frac{30}{36}$
and $\frac{7}{12} = \frac{21}{36}$.
So the order is:
$\frac{\mathbf{8}}{\mathbf{9}}, \frac{\mathbf{5}}{\mathbf{6}}, \frac{\mathbf{3}}{\mathbf{4}}, \frac{\mathbf{7}}{\mathbf{12}}$ *(1 mark)*

Q3 $\frac{\mathbf{13}}{\mathbf{15}}, \frac{\mathbf{11}}{\mathbf{8}}$ and $\frac{\mathbf{7}}{\mathbf{4}}$
should be circled.
(2 marks for all three correct, otherwise 1 mark for two correct.)

Q4 Make equivalent fractions with the same denominator:
Emily has eaten $\frac{5}{8} = \frac{15}{24}$ of her pizza.
Max has eaten $\frac{4}{6} = \frac{16}{24}$ of his pizza.

Ahmed has eaten $\frac{3}{4} = \frac{18}{24}$ of his pizza.
(1 mark for all equivalent fractions.)
So **Ahmed** has eaten the most pizza.
(1 mark)

Page 25 — Multiplying Fractions

Q1 $\frac{1}{6} \times \frac{1}{4} = \frac{1}{6 \times 4} = \frac{\mathbf{1}}{\mathbf{24}}$
$\frac{1}{11} \times \frac{1}{5} = \frac{1}{5 \times 11} = \frac{\mathbf{1}}{\mathbf{55}}$
(1 mark for both correct)

Q2 $\frac{4}{9} \times \frac{2}{9} = \frac{4 \times 2}{9 \times 9} = \frac{\mathbf{8}}{\mathbf{81}}$ *(1 mark)*

Q3 $\frac{2}{5} \times \frac{3}{4} = \frac{2 \times 3}{5 \times 4} = \frac{6}{20} = \frac{\mathbf{3}}{\mathbf{10}}$
(1 mark)

Q4 $\frac{4}{5} \times \frac{1}{3} = \frac{\mathbf{4}}{\mathbf{15}}$ *(1 mark)*
E.g. $\frac{\mathbf{2}}{\mathbf{3}} \times \frac{\mathbf{4}}{\mathbf{7}} = \frac{\mathbf{8}}{\mathbf{21}}$ *(1 mark)*

Pages 26-27 — Adding and Subtracting Fractions

Q1 $\frac{2}{5} + \frac{7}{15} = \frac{6}{15} + \frac{7}{15} = \frac{\mathbf{13}}{\mathbf{15}}$
(1 mark)
$\frac{2}{3} - \frac{11}{18} = \frac{12}{18} - \frac{11}{18} = \frac{\mathbf{1}}{\mathbf{18}}$
(1 mark)

Q2 $\frac{9}{8} + \frac{1}{5} = \frac{45}{40} + \frac{8}{40} = \frac{53}{40}$
$= \mathbf{1}\frac{\mathbf{13}}{\mathbf{40}}$ *(1 mark)*

Q3 $1\frac{3}{10} - \frac{5}{8} = \frac{13}{10} - \frac{5}{8} = \frac{52}{40} - \frac{25}{40}$
$= \frac{\mathbf{27}}{\mathbf{40}}$ of a litre
(2 marks for the correct answer. Otherwise 1 mark for putting fractions over a common denominator.)

Q4 $1\frac{3}{4} + 1\frac{1}{6} = \frac{7}{4} + \frac{7}{6}$
$= \frac{21}{12} + \frac{14}{12} = \frac{35}{12} = \mathbf{2}\frac{\mathbf{11}}{\mathbf{12}}$
(2 marks for the correct answer. Otherwise 1 mark for correct working.)

Q5 $\frac{2}{9} + \frac{5}{12} = \frac{8}{36} + \frac{15}{36} = \frac{23}{36}$
$1 - \frac{23}{36} = \frac{36}{36} - \frac{23}{36} = \frac{\mathbf{13}}{\mathbf{36}}$
(2 marks for the correct answer, otherwise 1 mark for finding the total amount of bread eaten.)

Q6 $3\frac{1}{6} + 1\frac{3}{10} - \frac{17}{15}$
$= \frac{19}{6} + \frac{13}{10} - \frac{17}{15}$
$= \frac{95}{30} + \frac{39}{30} - \frac{34}{30}$
$= \frac{100}{30} = \frac{\mathbf{10}}{\mathbf{3}}$
(2 marks for the correct answer, otherwise 1 mark for putting fractions over a common denominator.)

Q7 The Williams family use
$\frac{7}{10} + \frac{3}{5} + \frac{1}{4}$
$= \frac{14}{20} + \frac{12}{20} + \frac{5}{20} = \frac{\mathbf{31}}{\mathbf{20}}$ pints
(1 mark)
The Kang family use $1\frac{5}{8}$ pints.
$\frac{31}{20} = \frac{\mathbf{62}}{\mathbf{40}}$ and $1\frac{5}{8} = \frac{13}{8} = \frac{\mathbf{65}}{\mathbf{40}}$.
(1 mark)
So the **Kang** family use more milk in one day. *(1 mark)*

Page 28 — Dividing Fractions

Q1 $\frac{1}{3} \div 8 = \frac{1}{3 \times 8} = \frac{\mathbf{1}}{\mathbf{24}}$ *(1 mark)*
$\frac{1}{10} \div 7 = \frac{1}{10 \times 7} = \frac{\mathbf{1}}{\mathbf{70}}$
(1 mark)

Q2 $\frac{1}{2} \div 6 = \frac{1}{2 \times 6} = \frac{\mathbf{1}}{\mathbf{12}}$ *(1 mark)*

Q3 $\frac{8}{15} \div 4 = \frac{8}{15 \times 4} = \frac{8}{60} = \frac{\mathbf{2}}{\mathbf{15}}$
(1 mark)
$\frac{6}{7} \div 3 = \frac{6}{7 \times 3} = \frac{6}{21} = \frac{\mathbf{2}}{\mathbf{7}}$
(1 mark)

Q4 $\frac{6}{10} \div 4 = \frac{6}{10 \times 4} = \frac{6}{40} = \frac{\mathbf{3}}{\mathbf{20}}$
(1 mark)

Pages 29-30 — Equivalent Fractions and Decimals

Q1
$\frac{3}{10}$ 0.003
$\frac{3}{100}$ 0.3
$\frac{3}{1000}$ 0.03   *(1 mark)*

Q2 $0.007 = \frac{\mathbf{7}}{\mathbf{1000}}$, $\frac{19}{100} = \mathbf{0.19}$
$\frac{157}{1000} = \mathbf{0.157}$, $0.81 = \frac{\mathbf{81}}{\mathbf{100}}$
(2 marks for all four correct, otherwise 1 mark for two or three correct.)

Answers

Q3 $\frac{4}{5} = \frac{80}{100} = \mathbf{0.8}$

$\frac{13}{20} = \frac{65}{100} = \mathbf{0.65}$

$\frac{4}{25} = \frac{16}{100} = \mathbf{0.16}$

$\frac{29}{500} = \frac{58}{1000} = \mathbf{0.058}$

(2 marks for all four correct, otherwise 1 mark for two or three correct.)

Q4 $0.34 = \frac{34}{100} = \frac{17}{50}$ of a litre *(1 mark)*

Q5 $0.48 = \frac{48}{100} = \frac{12}{25}$ *(1 mark)*

Q6
$$8 \overline{)5\ ^50\ ^20\ ^40}$$
$$\ \ \ \ 6\ 2\ 5$$
$\frac{5}{8} = 625 \div 1000$
$= \mathbf{0.625}$ should be circled *(1 mark)*

Q7
$$8 \overline{)7\ ^70\ ^60\ ^40}$$
$$\ \ \ \ 8\ 7\ 5$$
(1 mark)
$\frac{7}{8} = 875 \div 1000 = \mathbf{0.875}$ *(1 mark)*

Pages 31-32 — Fractions, Decimals and Percentages

Q1 $\frac{4}{5} \rightarrow 0.8 \rightarrow \mathbf{80\%}$ *(1 mark)*

$\frac{3}{4} \rightarrow \mathbf{0.75} \rightarrow 75\%$ *(1 mark)*

$\frac{3}{10} \rightarrow 0.3 \rightarrow \mathbf{30\%}$ *(1 mark)*

Q2 $\frac{2}{5} > 0.39$ *(1 mark)*

$0.05 < \frac{3}{50}$ *(1 mark)*

$\frac{8}{25} = 0.32$ *(1 mark)*

Q3 $\frac{7}{20} = \frac{35}{100} = 0.35 = 35\%$ *(1 mark)*

So **Shoshanna** has decorated more cakes. *(1 mark)*

Q4 Sample working:
$\frac{22}{25} = 0.88$, $89\% = 0.89$,
$\frac{43}{50} = 0.86$, so the order is:
$\mathbf{0.85, \frac{43}{50}, \frac{22}{25}, 89\%}$

(2 marks for the correct order. Otherwise 1 mark for converting all values to decimals, percentages or fractions over the same denominator.)

Q5 Sample working:
$\frac{13}{20} = 0.65$, $62\% = 0.62$,
$\frac{39}{60} = \frac{13}{20} = 0.65$, $13\% = 0.13$,
$\frac{26}{50} = 0.52$, $\frac{3}{5} = 0.6$
So $\mathbf{0.65}$, $\mathbf{\frac{13}{20}}$ and $\mathbf{\frac{39}{60}}$ should be circled.
(2 marks for correct three amounts circled. Otherwise 1 mark for converting four or more values to decimals or percentages.)

Q6 $\frac{6}{25} = \frac{24}{100} = 24\%$ *(1 mark)*

So **Mr Barlow** has driven the greater distance *(1 mark)*.

Together they have driven $24\% + 27\% = 51\%$ of the distance, so there is $100\% - 51\% = \mathbf{49\%}$ of the journey left. *(1 mark)*

Section Four — Ratio, Proportion & Algebra

Pages 33-35 — Ratio and Proportion

Q1 $7 \times 50\ g = \mathbf{350\ g}$ *(1 mark)*

Q2 $345 \div 15 = \mathbf{23\ litres}$ *(1 mark)*

Q3 $24 \div 4 = 6$ boxes
$£3.60 \times 6 = \mathbf{£21.60}$ *(1 mark)*

Q4 $£2.40 \div 6 = \mathbf{£0.40}$ *(1 mark)*
$4 \times £0.40 = \mathbf{£1.60}$ *(1 mark)*

Q5 $\mathbf{7 : 3}$ *(1 mark)*
There are 4 triangles and 6 squares, so for every 2 triangles there are **3** squares. *(1 mark)*

Q6 $48 \div 12 = \mathbf{4}$ *(1 mark)*
$11 \times 12 = \mathbf{132}$ *(1 mark)*

Q7 $24 \div 8 = 3$
$3 \times 3 = \mathbf{9}$ *(1 mark)*

Q8 $27 \div 3 = 9$
$9 \times 7 = \mathbf{63}$ *(1 mark)*

Q9 $42 \div 6 = 7$
Number of girls $= 7 \times 7 = 49$ *(1 mark)*
Number of children $= 42 + 49 = \mathbf{91}$ *(1 mark)*

Q10 $6\ cm \div 2\ cm = 3$, so the distance in real life is $3 \times 100 = \mathbf{300\ m}$ *(1 mark)*

Q11 $50\ g \div 10\ g = 5$. So he is using 5 times the recipe.
$600\ g \times 5 = \mathbf{3000\ g}$ *(1 mark)*
$\frac{15}{20} = \frac{3}{4}$, so she is using $\frac{3}{4}$ of the recipe.
$10\ g \times \frac{3}{4} = \mathbf{7.5\ g}$ *(1 mark)*

Pages 36-37 — Unequal Sharing

Q1 There are $1 + 4 = 5$ shares.
So Ivan gets $\frac{1}{5}$. *(1 mark)*

Q2 There are $3 + 2 = 5$ shares.
1 share $= 35 \div 5 = 7$
Fleur: $7 \times 3 = \mathbf{21}$ grapes
Bridget: $7 \times 2 = \mathbf{14}$ grapes *(1 mark)*

Q3 There are $4 + 3 = 7$ shares.
1 share $= 63 \div 7 = 9$
Roger: $9 \times 3 = \mathbf{27}$ points. *(1 mark)*

Q4 There are $9 + 5 = 14$ shares.
1 share $= 98 \div 14 = 7$
Aki: $7 \times 9 = 63$ windows
Gemma: $7 \times 5 = 35$ windows
Difference $= 63 - 35 = \mathbf{28}$
(2 marks for the correct answer. Otherwise 1 mark for finding the number of windows cleaned by Aki or by Gemma.)

Q5 There are $1 + 4 + 5 = 10$ shares.
1 share $= £200 \div 10 = £20$
Andy: $£20 \times 1 = \mathbf{£20}$
Jenny: $£20 \times 4 = \mathbf{£80}$
Heather: $£20 \times 5 = \mathbf{£100}$
(2 marks for all correct amounts. Otherwise 1 mark for one correct amount.)

Q6 For every 2 white chocolates there is 1 milk chocolate.
There are $2 + 1 = 3$ shares.
1 share $= 42 \div 3 = 14$
$14 \times 2 = \mathbf{28}$ *(1 mark)*

Answers

Q7 $12 \div 3 = 4$
For every parcel the postman delivered, he delivered **4** letters. *(1 mark)*
$4 + 1 = 5$
$55 \div 5 = 11$
Parcels: $11 \times 1 = $ **11** *(1 mark)*
Letters: $11 \times 4 = $ **44** *(1 mark)*

Pages 38-41— Percentage Problems

Q1 10% of $390 = 390 \div 10 = $ **39**
1% of 6800
$= 6800 \div 100 = $ **68** *(1 mark)*

Q2 10% of $740 = 740 \div 10 = 74$
5% of $740 = 74 \div 2 = $ **37**
(1 mark)
10% of 2180
$= 2180 \div 10 = 218$
5% of $2180 = 218 \div 2 = 109$
15% of 2180
$= 218 + 109 = $ **327** *(1 mark)*

Q3 10% of $560 = 560 \div 10 = 56$
5% of $560 = 56 \div 2 = 28$
30% of $560 = 56 \times 3 = 168$
35% of 560
$= 168 + 28 = $ **196** *(1 mark)*

Q4 10% of £420
$= £420 \div 10 = £42$
5% of £420 $= £42 \div 2 = £21$
40% of £420 $= £42 \times 4$
$= £168$
$45\% = 168 + 21 = $ **£189**
(1 mark)

Q5 10% of $860 = 860 \div 10 = 86$
5% of $860 = 86 \div 2 = 43$
30% of $860 = 86 \times 3 = 258$
35% of $860 = 258 + 43$
$= $ **301** *(1 mark)*

$45\% + 15\% = 60\%$
10% of $860 = 860 \div 10 = 86$
50% of $860 = 860 \div 2 = 430$
60% of 860
$= 86 + 430 = $ **516** *(1 mark)*

Q6 10% of $300 = 300 \div 10 = 30$
30% of $300 = 30 \times 3 = 90$
1% of $300 = 300 \div 100 = 3$
2% of $300 = 3 \times 2 = 6$
32% of $300 = 90 + 6 = $ **96**
(1 mark)

Q7 Saturday:
10% of $400 = 400 \div 10 = 40$
40% of $400 = 40 \times 4 = 160$
5% of $400 = 40 \div 2 = 20$
45% of 400
$= 160 + 20 = 180$

Sunday:
50% of $700 = 700 \div 2 = 350$
1% of $700 = 700 \div 100 = 7$
8% of $700 = 7 \times 8 = 56$
58% of 700
$= 350 + 56 = 406$
Total: $406 + 180 = $ **586**
(3 marks for the correct answer. Otherwise 1 mark for finding 45% of 400 and 1 mark for finding 58% of 700.)

Q8 $\frac{11}{25} = \frac{44}{100} = $ **44%** *(1 mark)*

$\frac{7}{20} = \frac{35}{100} = $ **35%** *(1 mark)*

Q9 $\frac{9}{15} = \frac{3}{5} = $ **60%** *(1 mark)*

Q10 $7 + 20 + 8 = 35$ marbles.
$\frac{7}{35} = \frac{1}{5} = $ **20%** *(1 mark)*

Q11 $\frac{12}{20} = \frac{60}{100} = $ **60%** *(1 mark)*

Q12 £3500 – £2000
$= £1500$ profit
$\frac{1500}{2000} = \frac{150}{200} = \frac{75}{100} = $ **75%**
(2 marks for the correct answer. Otherwise 1 mark for finding the profit.)

Q13 Stuart's percentage profit:
$\frac{160}{800} = \frac{20}{100} = 20\%$
Miranda's percentage profit:
$\frac{60}{250} = \frac{12}{50} = \frac{24}{100} = 24\%$
(1 mark)
24% > 20% so **Miranda** made the highest percentage profit. *(1 mark)*

Q14 Nutios increase:
$750\,g - 600\,g = 150\,g$
$\frac{150}{600} = \frac{50}{200} = \frac{25}{100} = 25\%$
Branpops increase:
$360\,g - 300\,g = 60\,g$
$\frac{60}{300} = \frac{20}{100} = 20\%$ *(1 mark)*
Nutios are increasing by the highest percentage.
(1 mark)

Pages 42-43 — Similar Shapes

Q1
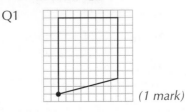 *(1 mark)*

Q2
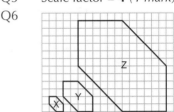
(1 mark)

Q3 $14 \times 8 = $ **112 cm** *(1 mark)*

Q4 $72 \div 6 = $ **12 cm** *(1 mark)*

Q5 Scale factor = **4** *(1 mark)*

Q6
(1 mark for each correctly enlarged shape.)
Scale factor = **6** *(1 mark)*

Pages 44-45 — Formulas and Expressions

Q1 Number of slides =
6 × number of packs
(1 mark)
Number of packs =
number of slides ÷ 6
(1 mark)

Q2 Total cost =
28 × number of cupcakes +
$36 \times$ **number of doughnuts**
(1 mark)

Q3 Amount of pasta =
30 × number of guests
(1 mark)
$30 \times 120 = 3600$ grams
$3600 \div 1000 = 3.6$
So 3600 grams = **3.6 kg**
(2 marks for the correct answer. Otherwise 1 mark for working out the amount needed in grams.)

Q4 Rare:
$\frac{1500}{20} + 15 = \frac{150}{2} + 15$
$= 75 + 15 = $ **90 mins**
(1 mark)
Well done:
$\frac{1500}{15} + 35$
$= 100 + 35 = 135$ mins
Extra time $= 135 - 90$
$= $ **45 mins** *(1 mark)*

Answers

Q5 The total number of points is given by: **5 × number of goals + 3 × number of penalties** *(1 mark)*

$5 \times 7 + 3 \times 4 = 35 + 12$ = **47 points** *(1 mark)*

Page 46 — Finding Missing Numbers 1

Q1 $y = 3 \times 7 = \mathbf{21}$ *(1 mark)*

$36 = 3x$
$x = 36 \div 3 = \mathbf{12}$ *(1 mark)*

Q2 $11 \times \triangle + 7 = 40$
$11 \times \triangle = 33$
So $\triangle = 33 \div 11 = \mathbf{3}$
(1 mark)

$35 \div 7 - \stackrel{\wedge}{\star} = -1$
$5 - \stackrel{\wedge}{\star} = -1$
So $\stackrel{\wedge}{\star} = \mathbf{6}$ *(1 mark)*

Q3 $22 \div 2 - 3$
$= 11 - 3 = \mathbf{8}$ *(1 mark)*

Q4 Elsa has m DVDs
Brita has 8m DVDs
Dani has **8m – 6** DVDs
(1 mark)
$8 \times 9 - 6 = \mathbf{66}$ *(1 mark)*

Pages 47-48 — Finding Missing Numbers 2

Q1

	⬠	☆
Pair 1	2	4
Pair 2	4	3
Pair 3	6	2
Pair 4	8	1

(2 marks for 4 correct pairs. Otherwise 1 mark for 2 correct pairs.)

Q2 Some possible pairs are:
If M = **1**, 5M = 5,
so 5 + N = 18 and N = **13**
If M = **2**, 5M = 10,
so 10 + N = 18 and N = **8**
If M = **3**, 5M = 15,
so 15 + N = 18 and N = **3**

	M	N
Pair 1	1	4
Pair 2	4	3
Pair 3	6	2

(2 marks for 3 correct pairs. Otherwise 1 mark for 2 correct pairs.)

Q3 Try multiplying different pairs of numbers that add up to 12:
$1 + 11 = 12$, $1 \times 11 = 11$
$2 + 10 = 12$, $2 \times 10 = 20$
$3 + 9 = 12$, $3 \times 9 = 27$
So Angelo's numbers are **3** and **9** *(1 mark)*.

Q4 $8A + 5B = 44$
Use trial and error to find:
$8 \times 3 + 5 \times 4 = 24 + 20 = 44$
So A = **3** and B = **4**. *(1 mark)*

Q5 $2b + 3k = 20$
b = **1**, k = **6**
b = **4**, k = **4**
b = **7**, k = **2**
(2 marks for 3 correct pairs. Otherwise 1 mark for 2 correct pairs.)

Q6 **2b = g** should be circled. *(1 mark)*

Q7 $A + A + A + B + B = C + C$
$3A + 2B = 11 + 11$
$3A + 2B = 22$
So the possible pairs are:
A = **2**, B = **8**
A = **4**, B = **5**
A = **6**, B = **2**
(2 marks for 3 correct pairs. Otherwise 1 mark for 2 correct pairs.)

Pages 49-50 — Number Sequences

Q1 $11 - 4 = 7$, $18 - 11 = 7$
The rule is **add 7**. *(1 mark)*

$55 - 49 = 6$, $49 - 43 = 6$
The rule is **take away 6**. *(1 mark)*

Q2 The rule is add 11.
3, 14, 25, **36**, **47**, **58** *(1 mark)*

The rule is take away 5.
23, 18, 13, **8**, **3**, **–2** *(1 mark)*

Q3 The rule is add 7.
2, 9, **16**, 23, 30, **37** *(1 mark)*

Q4 The rule is add 9.
–17, **–8**, 1, 10, **19** *(1 mark)*

The rule is take away 8.
1, **–7**, –15, –23, **–31** *(1 mark)*

Q5 The rule is add 4.
3, 7, 11, 15, 19, 23, 27, 31, 35, 39...
So the 10th term is **39**.
(1 mark)

Q6 The rule is multiply by 2.
2, 4, 8, 16, **32**, **64** *(1 mark)*

Q7 $2 \times 10 = 20$, $20 \times 10 = 200$
So the rule is **multiply by 10**.
(1 mark)

$48 \div 2 = 24$, $24 \div 2 = 12$
So the rule is **divide by 2**.
(1 mark)

Q8 The difference between 6 and –2 is 8.
There are 2 steps between 6 and –2 so $8 \div 2 = 4$.
The rule is subtract 4.
6, **2**, –2, **–6**, –10 *(1 mark for each correct term.)*

Section Five — Measure

Pages 51-54 — Units and Conversions

Q1 **1 cm**, **300 mm**, **800 g** and **5 g** should be circled.
(2 marks for all correct. Otherwise 1 mark for 2 or 3 circled correctly.)

Q2 1 litre = 1000 ml
$8.7 \times 1000 = \mathbf{8700\ ml}$
(1 mark)
1 kg = 1000 g
$2500 \div 1000 = \mathbf{2.5\ kg}$
(1 mark)

Q3 $500 \times 10 = 5000$ m
1 km = 1000 m
$5000 \div 1000 = \mathbf{5\ km}$ *(1 mark)*

Q4 1 year = 365 days,
1 week = 7 days
So a year and 2 weeks
$= 365 + 7 + 7 = \mathbf{379\ days}$
(1 mark)

Q5 10 rubber balls would weigh
$10 \times 2 = 20$ ounces
$= \mathbf{1\ lb\ 4\ oz}$.
(2 marks for the correct answer. Otherwise 1 mark for the weight of 10 rubber balls in ounces.)

Q6 1 km = 1000 m
$0.9 \times 1000 = 900$ m
$900 \div 150 = \mathbf{6}$ *(1 mark)*

Q7 1 cm = 10 mm
$5.3 \times 10 = 53$ mm
$4.7 \times 10 = 47$ mm
$40 + 53 + 47 = \mathbf{140\ mm}$
(1 mark)

Answers

Q8 1 litre = 1000 ml
3 × 1000 = 3000 ml
3000 ÷ 2 = **1500 ml**
(1 mark)

Q9 72.4 kg = 72.4 × 1000
= 72 400 g
69.2 kg = 69.2 × 1000
= 69 200 g
72 400 g − 69 200 g
= **3200 g** *(1 mark)*

Q10 15 × 4 = 60 seconds
= 1 minute
30 + 45 = 75 seconds
60 seconds = 1 minute,
so 75 secs
= 60 seconds + 15 seconds
= 1 minute 15 seconds
Total length = 1 minute +
1 minute 15 seconds =
2 minutes 15 seconds
*(2 marks for correct answer.
Otherwise 1 mark for
working with no more than
one error.)*

Q11 45 + 22 = 67 minutes.
1 hour = 60 minutes
3 hours = 3 × 60
= 180 minutes
180 − 67 = **113 minutes**
*(2 marks for correct answer.
Otherwise 1 mark for
working with no more than
one error.)*

Q12 5 miles ≈ 8 km
320 ÷ 8 = 40
40 × 5 = 200 miles
So 320 km ≈ **200 miles**.
(1 mark)

Q13 4.5 + 1.3 + 1.7 = 7.5 miles
5 miles ≈ 8 km
7.5 ÷ 5 = 1.5
1.5 × 8 = **12 km** *(1 mark)*
1 kg = 1000 g
24 × 1000 = 24 000 g
24 000 ÷ 12 = **2000**
*(2 marks for correct answer.
Otherwise 1 mark for
converting 24 grams to kg.)*

Q14 1 km = 1000 m
18 × 1000 = 18 000 m
1 hour = 60 minutes
18 000 m per hour ÷ 60
= **300 m per minute**
*(2 marks for correct answer.
Otherwise 1 mark for
working with no more than
one error.)*

Pages 55-56 — Perimeters and Areas

Q1 6 equal sides, so perimeter
= 3 × 6 = **18 cm** *(1 mark)*

8 equal sides, so perimeter
= 2 × 8 = **16 m** *(1 mark)*

Q2 Perimeter:
6 + 2 + 6 + 2 + 6 + 2 + 6 + 2
= **32 cm** *(1 mark)*

Area = length × width
Length = 2 + 6 + 2 = 10 cm
Area = 10 × 6 = **60 cm²**
(1 mark)

Q3 Area of A = 8 × 4 = 32 cm²
Area of B = 9 × 4 = 36 cm²
Area of C = 13 × 3 = 39 cm²
Area of D = 6 × 6 = 36 cm²
Area of E = 18 × 2 = 36 cm²
So **B**, **D** and **E** should be
circled. *(1 mark)*

Q4

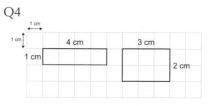

*(1 mark — rectangles may be
drawn rotated 90°.)*

Q5 Area = length × width,
so width = area ÷ length
Width of rectangle A
= 18 ÷ 9 = 2 cm
Perimeter of rectangle A
= 9 + 2 + 9 + 2 = **22 cm**
(1 mark)

Length of rectangle B
= 18 ÷ 3 = 6 cm
Perimeter of rectangle B
= 6 + 3 + 6 + 3 = **18 cm**
(1 mark)

Q6 Missing measurements:
10 − 6 = 4 m
14 − 9 = 5 m
Perimeter:
14 + 10 + 9 + 4 + 5 + 6
= **48 m** *(1 mark)*

Split shape into 2 rectangles
and add their areas, e.g:
5 × 6 = 30 m²
9 × 10 = 90 m²
30 + 90 = **120 m²** *(1 mark)*

Pages 57-58 — Areas of Triangles

Q1 A = ½ × base × height
= ½ × 12 × 10
= **60 mm²** *(1 mark)*

A = ½ × base × height
= ½ × 7 m × 4 m
= **14 m²** *(1 mark)*

Q2 Area of left-hand triangle
= ½ × base × height
= ½ × 2 × 5
= 5 cm²
Area of right-hand triangle
= ½ × base × height
= ½ × 3 × 5
= 7.5 cm²
Total = 5 + 7.5 = **12.5 cm²**
(1 mark)

Q3 Area of square
= base × height
= 8 × 8 = 64 cm²
Area of one triangle
= ½ × base × height
= ½ × 8 × 8
= 32 cm²
Area of four triangles
= 32 × 4 = 128 cm²
Total area:
64 + 128 = **192 cm²** *(1 mark)*

Q4 Area of square = 3 × 3 = 9 m²
Triangle height = 5 − 3 = 2 m
Area of triangle
= ½ × 3 × 2 = 3 m²
Total area = 9 + 3 = **12 m²**
*(2 marks for correct answer.
Otherwise 1 mark for correct
area of triangle or square.)*

Q5 Split the square up into 4
triangles:

Area of one triangle
= ½ × 6 × 6 = 18 cm²
There are 4 triangles, so
area of square
= 18 × 4 = **72 cm²**
*(2 marks for correct answer.
Otherwise 1 mark for
calculating the area of one
triangle.)*

Answers

Q6 Each triangle has area
= ½ × 7 × 8 = 28 cm²
Each tile has 2 triangles, so
grey area on one tile is:
28 × 2 = 56 cm²
There are 100 tiles, so the
total grey area is:
56 × 100 = **5600 cm²**.
*(2 marks for correct answer.
Otherwise 1 mark for
correct area of triangle)*

Page 59 —
Areas of Parallelograms

Q1 Area = base × height
= 3 × 2 = **6 mm²** *(1 mark)*
Area = 7 × 13 = **91 m²**
(1 mark)

Q2 Area of left-hand
parallelogram
= 8 × 6 = 48 cm²
Area of right-hand
parallelogram
= 8 × 8 = 64 cm²
48 + 64 = **112 cm²**
*(2 marks for correct answer.
Otherwise 1 mark for correct
area of one parallelogram.)*

Q3 Each white arrow is made
up of two parallelograms of
height 4 ÷ 2 = 2 m.
Area of one parallelogram
= 1 × 2 = 2 m².
So area of one arrow
= 2 × 2 = 4 m²
There are two white arrows,
so total white area
= 2 × 4 = 8 m²
Area of sign = 6 × 4 = 24 m²
Area of sign that is **not** white
= 24 − 8 = **16 m²** *(3 marks
for correct answer, otherwise
1 mark for correct area of a
parallelogram and 1 mark for
correct area of an arrow)*

Pages 60-61 — Volume

Q1 Volume = l × w × h
= 8 × 2 × 5
= **80 cm³** *(1 mark)*

Volume = l × w × h
= 10 × 2 × 2
= **40 mm³** *(1 mark)*

Q2 The box with the largest
volume will hold the most.
Volume of Box A = l × w × h
= 20 × 20 × 20 = 8000 cm³

Volume of Box B = l × w × h
= 25 × 30 × 10 = 7500 cm³
(1 mark)
So **Box A** will hold the most.
(1 mark)

Q3 Volume = l × w × h
= 20 × 5 × 2 = **200 m³**
(1 mark)

Q4 Split the shape up into 2
cuboids, then add their
volumes, e.g:
Volume of cuboid 1:
l × w × h = 3 × 4 × 5
= 60 cm³
Volume of cuboid 2:
l × w × h = 3 × 3 × 7
= 63 cm³
Total volume = 60 + 63
= **123 cm³** *(2 marks for
correct answer, otherwise 1
mark for 1 correct volume)*

Q5 Volume of wooden cuboid
= l × w × h = 5 × 3 × 2
= 30 m³
Volume of hole = l × w × h
= 5 × 1 × 1 = 5 m³
Volume of wood = 30 − 5
= **25 m³** *(2 marks for correct
answer Otherwise 1 mark for
1 correct volume)*

Section Six — Geometry
Pages 62-63 —
Angle Rules

Q1 c = a = **103°** (vertically
opposite angles) *(1 mark)*
b = 180° − 103° = **77°**
(angles on a straight line)
(1 mark)
d = b = **77°** (vertically
opposite angles) *(1 mark)*

Q2 A = 180° − 38° − 112° = **30°**
(1 mark)
B = 180° − 69° − 88° = **23°**
(1 mark)

Q3 A = 360° − 108° − 138°
= **114°** *(1 mark)*
B = 360° − 33° − 90° − 117°
= **120°** *(1 mark)*

Q4 360° ÷ 5 = **72°** *(1 mark)*

Q5 Q = 360° − 25° − 113° − 67° −
35° = **120°** *(1 mark)*

Q6 x = **48°** (vertically opposite
angles) *(1 mark)*

y = 180° − 30° − 48° = **102°**
(angles on a straight line)
(1 mark)

Q7 A = **62°** (vertically opposite
angles) *(1 mark)*
B = 180° − 28° = **152°**
(angles on a straight line)
(1 mark)

Pages 64-65 —
Drawing 2D Shapes

Q1 All angles should be 90° to
within 1°. All sides should
be correct to within 1 mm.

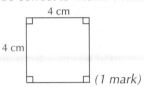

(1 mark)

Q2 All angles should be 90° to
within 1°. All sides should
be correct to within 1 mm.

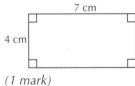

(1 mark)

Q3 All angles should be 60° to
within 1°. All sides should
be correct to within 1 mm.

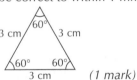

(1 mark)

Q4 The angle between the two
shorter sides of the triangle
should be 90° to within 1°.
All sides should be correct to
within 1 mm.

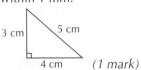

(1 mark)

Q5 All angles should be 120° to
within 1°. All sides should
be correct to within 1 mm.

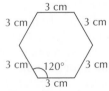

*(2 marks. Otherwise
1 mark for four sides and
three angles correct.)*

Answers

Q6 All angles should be correct to within 1°. All sides should be correct to within 1 mm.

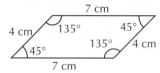

(2 marks. Otherwise 1 mark for two sides and one angle correct.)

Pages 66-67 — Properties of Shapes

Q1 A square has **4** right angles.
A trapezium has one pair of **parallel** sides.
An equilateral triangle has three angles of **60°**.
(2 marks for all gaps filled correctly. Otherwise 1 mark for one or two gaps filled correctly.)

Q2 **Rectangle — 2 pairs of equal-length sides and 4 equal angles.**
Kite — 2 pairs of equal-length sides and 1 pair of equal angles.
Rhombus — 4 equal-length sides and 2 pairs of equal angles.
Parallelogram — 2 pairs of equal-length sides and 2 pairs of equal angles.
(2 marks for all correct matches, otherwise 1 mark for two correct matches.)

Q3 The **circumference** of the circle is 20 cm. *(1 mark)*

Q4 E.g.

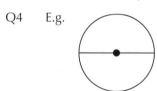

(1 mark for a line drawn from one side of the circle to the other, through the centre.)

Q5 The radius of circle B is 2 × 14 = 28 cm.
The diameter of the second circle is d = 2 × r = **56 cm** *(1 mark)*

Q6 E.g.

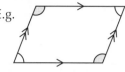

(2 marks. 1 mark for either pair of opposite angles shaded, 1 mark for matching arrows on both pairs of parallel sides.)

Q7 d = 2 × r
30 = 2 × r
30 ÷ 2 = r
so r = **15 cm** *(1 mark)*
x = 15 − 12 = **3 cm** *(1 mark)*

Pages 68-69 — Angles in Shapes

Q1 x = 180° − 76° − 39° = **65°**
(1 mark)

Q2 y = 360° − 97° − 122° − 74°
= **67°** *(1 mark)*

Q3 a + b + 38° = 180°
a + b = 142°
It is an isosceles triangle, so a and b are equal.
142° ÷ 2 = 71°
So a = b = **71°** *(1 mark)*

Q4 A rhombus has two pairs of equal angles, and the angles in a quadrilateral add up to 360°.
So, 52° + 52° + x + x = 360°
104° + 2x = 360°
2x = 256°, x = **128°**
(2 marks for correct answer, otherwise 1 mark for using properties of a rhombus.)

Q5 Exterior angle
= 360° ÷ number of sides
= 360° ÷ 9 = **40°** *(1 mark)*
Interior angle
= 180° − exterior angle
= 180° − 40° = **140°**
(1 mark)

Q6 Sum of interior angles
= (n − 2) × 180°
= 6 × 180° = **1080°** *(1 mark)*
One interior angle
= 1080° ÷ 8 = **135°** *(1 mark)*

Q7 Sum of interior angles
= 3 × 180° = **540°** *(1 mark)*
x = 540° − 146° − 63° − 98°
− 120° = **113°** *(1 mark)*

Pages 70-71 — 3D Shapes

Q1 A cube has **6** faces.
(1 mark)
The net of a square-based pyramid has **4** triangles and one **square**. *(1 mark)*

Q2 **regular tetrahedron** or **equilateral triangle-based pyramid** *(1 mark)*
triangular prism *(1 mark)*

Q3

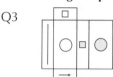

(2 marks for all symbols correct, otherwise 1 mark for three or more symbols correct.)

Q4 E.g.

(1 mark)

Q5

should be circled.
(1 mark)

Q6 E.g.

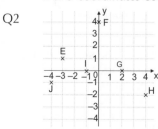

(1 mark)

Pages 72-73 — Coordinates

Q1 Point A **(–2, 3)**,
Point B **(3, 0)**
Point C **(1, –4)**,
Point D **(–1, –1)**
(2 marks for all coordinates correct, otherwise 1 mark for 2 or 3 coordinates correct.)

Q2

(2 marks for all points plotted correctly, otherwise 1 mark for four or five points correct.)

Answers

Q3 The two given points are 7 units apart on the x-axis, so the side-length is 7.
So, point A is **(5, 5)** and point B is **(–2, –2)**.
(1 mark)

Q4 The rectangle has a base of 6 units and a height of 3 units, so M is (7 + 6, 9 – 3) = **(13, 6)**. *(1 mark)*

Q5 The point (–3, 4) is 4 units to the left and 2 units down from the point (1, 6).
P is the same distance from (1, 6), but to the right, so P is (1 + 4, 6 – 2) = **(5, 4)**.
(1 mark)

Q6 Point T is in line horizontally with (0, 4), so it has the same y-coordinate. The length of the longer sides of the parallelogram is 6 units. T is twice as far as this horizontally from the point (0, 4), so its x-coordinate is 12. T is **(12, 4)**. *(1 mark)*

Pages 74-75 — Reflection

Q1
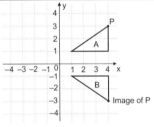
(1 mark)
The coordinates of the image of P are **(4, –3)**.
(1 mark)

Q2
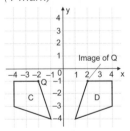
(1 mark)
The coordinates of the image of Q are **(2, –1)**.
(1 mark)

Q3
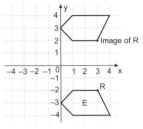
(1 mark)

Q4 Reflection in the y-axis changes the sign of the x-coordinate, but doesn't change the y-coordinate. So the image of M is **(–4, –1)**. *(1 mark)*

Q5
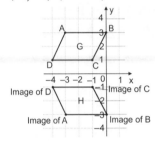
(1 mark)
Image of A: **(–3, 3)**
Image of B: **(0, –3)**
Image of C: **(–1, –1)**
Image of D: **(–4, –1)**
(1 mark)

Q6
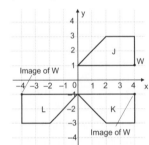
(2 marks. 1 mark for each reflection.)
The coordinates of W on shape L are **(–4, –1)**.
(1 mark)

Pages 76-77 — Translation

Q1
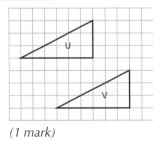
(1 mark)

Q2
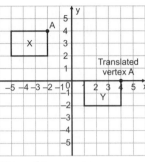
(1 mark)
The coordinates of vertex A on shape Y are **(4, 0)**.
(1 mark)

Q3
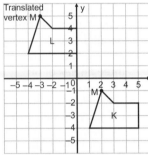
(1 mark)
The coordinates of vertex M on shape L are **(–3, 5)**.
(1 mark)

Q4 The x-coordinate of the translated vertex Z on shape P is –3 – 1 = –4.
The y-coordinate is 2 + 4 = 6.
So the translated vertex Z has coordinates **(–4, 6)**.
(1 mark)

Q5 **+5** units horizontally **+4** units vertically *(1 mark)*

Q6 Point P is (a, b) = (4, 1) The translated point P is (a – 6, b + 1) = (4 – 6, 1 + 1) = **(–2, 2)**. *(1 mark)*

Q7 (a + 1, b + 2) = (–2 + 1, 4 + 2) = **(–1, 6)**
(1 mark)

Section Seven — Statistics

Pages 78-79 — Line Graphs

Q1 Reading from the graph, Billy's mass at 2 months is **70 g** *(1 mark)*

Answers

Plot Fred's mass against his age as shown on the graph below:

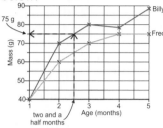

(2 marks for correct points plotted and joined. Otherwise 1 mark for at least two points plotted correctly.)

Reading from the graph (see above) Billy's mass at 2 and a half months is **75 g**. *(1 mark)*

Billy's mass drops **between 3 and 4 months**, so this is likely to be when he was ill. *(1 mark)*

Q2 Reading from the graph, 3 dollars = **£2** *(1 mark)*

Reading from the graph, £4 = **$6** *(1 mark)*

Q3 Reading from the graph, the snow was deepest at **10:00 am** *(1 mark)*

Reading from the graph, the snow was 1 cm deep at 8:30 am and 4 cm deep at 9 am. So it got 4 – 1 = **3 cm** deeper. *(1 mark)*

Pages 80-81 — Pie Charts

Q1 The beach and funfair are each ¼ of the pie chart, so there were 48 ÷ 4 = 12 votes for each.
The zoo section is half of ¼, so it got 12 ÷ 2 = 6 votes.
The waterpark section is the same size as the beach section and the zoo section added together, so it got 12 + 6 = 18 votes.

Trip destination	Number of votes
Zoo	6
Funfair	12
Waterpark	18
Beach	12

(2 marks for completely correct table, otherwise 1 mark for two correct values.)

Q2 The pizza section is $\frac{1}{6}$.
$\frac{1}{6}$ = 20 children, so altogether there must be
6 × 20 = **120 children**
(1 mark)

The sandwich section is $\frac{1}{4}$ of the pie chart, so
120 ÷ 4 = 30 children chose a sandwich.
The curry section is $\frac{1}{6}$ of the pie chart, so
120 ÷ 6 = 20 children chose curry.
30 – 20 = **10 children**
(1 mark)

Q3 360° ÷ 10 = **36°** *(1 mark)*

36° × 2 = **72°** *(1 mark)*

Q4 Multiplier = 360 ÷ 60 = 6

Superhero	Number of children	Angle
Turnip Man	15	15 × 6 = **90°**
Thunder Smash	30	30 × 6 = **180°**
Magic Mary	10	10 × 6 = **60°**
Bolt Girl	5	5 × 6 = **30°**

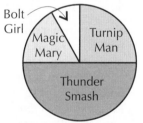

(2 marks for table and pie chart completely correct, otherwise 1 mark for at least 2 angles correctly calculated or correctly drawn in the pie chart.)

Q5 Sparrow angle = 60°
$\frac{60}{360} = \frac{6}{36} = \frac{1}{6}$
$\frac{1}{6}$ of the birds are sparrows, so Holly recorded 120 ÷ 6 = **20 sparrows** *(1 mark)*

Wren angle = 30°
$\frac{30}{360} = \frac{3}{36} = \frac{1}{12}$
$\frac{1}{12}$ of the birds are wrens, so Holly recorded 120 ÷ 12 = **10 wrens** *(1 mark)*

Multiplier = 360 ÷ 120 = 3.
There were 4 jackdaws, so the jackdaw section should be 4 × 3 = **12°** *(1 mark)*

Pages 82-83 — The Mean

Q1 Total = 8 + 4 + 5 + 7 = 24
Mean = 24 ÷ 4 = **6** *(1 mark)*
Total = 3 + 12 + 11 + 5 + 20 + 15 = 66
Mean = 66 ÷ 6 = **11** *(1 mark)*

Q2 Total mass =
40 + 55 + 50 + 60 + 45
= **250 g** *(1 mark)*
Mean mass = 250 ÷ 5 = **50 g**
(1 mark)

Q3 Read the daily number of photos from the graph and add to find the total:
40 + 10 + 20 + 25 + 5 = 100
Mean = 100 ÷ 5 = **20**
(1 mark)

Q4 Total = 55 + 125 + 90 + 110 = 380p
Mean = 380 ÷ 4 = **95p**
(1 mark)
If the mean doesn't change, the new cake's price must be equal to the mean, so it's **95p**. *(1 mark)*

Q5 8 packets with 3 slices
= 8 × 3 = 24 slices
5 packets with 4 slices
= 5 × 4 = 20 slices
6 packets with 5 slices
= 6 × 5 = 30 slices
1 packet with 6 slices
= 1 × 6 = 6 slices
Total number of slices
= 24 + 20 + 30 + 6 = **80**
(1 mark)

The mean = 80 ÷ 20 = 4, so the claim on the packet is not correct.
(1 mark for calculating the mean and 1 mark for stating that the claim is incorrect.)

Q6 There are 6 pupils and the mean mark is 7, so the total should be 6 × 7 = 42 marks. The total marks for 5 of the pupils is 5 + 8 + 10 + 8 + 7 = 38. So the 7th mark must be 42 – 38 = **4**.
(2 marks for correct answer. Otherwise 1 mark for finding the total number of marks.)

Answers

Test 2 — Pages 84-87

Q1
$$22 \overline{\smash{\big)}\,4\;6\;8\;6}$$
    2 1 3

  − 4 4

       2 8

    − 2 2

          6 6

      − 6 6

             0

(1 mark)

Q2 **1.074, 1.407, 1.450, 1.7, 1.705** *(1 mark)*

Q3 The horizontal parts of the graph represent when Stephanie is not moving. Each small square represents 5 minutes horizontally. So Stephanie waits for:
$(2 \times 5) + (1 \times 5)$
= **15 minutes** *(1 mark)*

Stephanie reaches her office 55 minutes after 7:15 am. Add on 1 hour and subtract 5 minutes:
7:15 + 1 hour = 8:15
8:15 − 5 minutes = **8:10 am**
(1 mark)

Q4 Factors of 12: 1, 2, 3, 4, 6, 12
Factors of 18: 1, 2, 3, 6, 9, 18
Factors of 30: 1, 2, 3, 5, 6, 10, 15, 30
The highest number that appears in all three lists is **6**
(1 mark)

Q5 Area of rectangle
= length × width =
= 12 × 7 = 84 cm²
Area of triangle
= ½ × base × height
= ½ × 12 × 3
= 6 × 3 = 18 cm²
(1 mark for both areas)
Shaded area = 84 − 18
= **66 cm²** *(1 mark)*

Q6 Sarah walked M km on Monday, 2M km on Tuesday, and 3M km on Wednesday.
So M + 2M + 3M = 30.6 km, then 6M = 30.6 km and
M = **5.1 km** *(1 mark for correct answer and 1 mark for some correct working shown.)*

Q7 It takes 3 °C to get to 0 °C
That leaves 12 − 3 = 9 °C
So −3 °C + 12 °C = **9 °C**
(1 mark)

Q8

Fraction	Decimal	Percentage
$\frac{9}{100}$	0.09	9%
$\frac{4}{5}$	0.8	80%
$\frac{3}{8}$	0.375	37.5%

Working:
$$8 \overline{\smash{\big)}\,3\;{}^3 0\;{}^6 0\;{}^4 0}$$
    3 7 5

so, $\frac{3}{8}$ = 0.375
(2 marks for completely correct table. Otherwise 1 mark for any 3 values correct.)

Q9 Angles on a straight line add up to 180°.
So a = 180° − 107° = **73°**

A parallelogram has two pairs of equal angles and the angles in a quadrilateral add up to 360°. So:
112° + 112° + b + b = 360°
224° + 2b = 360°
2b = 360° − 224° = 136°
So b = 136° ÷ 2 = **68°**

The angle on a straight line with c is 112° as diagonally opposite angles in a parallelogram are equal.
So c = 180° − 112° = **68°**
(2 marks for all three angles correct. Otherwise 1 mark for one or two angles correct.)

Q10 The number of packs produced is 600 ÷ 1.2
Calculate 600 ÷ 12 first.
$$12 \overline{\smash{\big)}\,6\;{}^6 0\;0}$$
      5 0

12 is 10 times larger than 1.2, so multiply by 10.
50 × 10 = **500** *(1 mark)*

The pet shop pays
£2.35 × 48
First calculate 235 × 48
     2 3 5
×   4 8
  1 8₂ 8₄ 0
  9₁ 4₂ 0 0
1₁ 1₁ 2 8 0

235 is 100 times larger than 2.35, so divide by 100.
£11 280 ÷ 100 = **£112.80**
(1 mark)

Q11

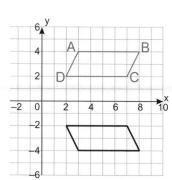

(1 mark)

Q12 Total number of snails =
6 + 9 + 11 + 10 + 7 + 8 + 9 + 4 = 64
There are 8 numbers, so
mean = 64 ÷ 8 = **8** *(1 mark)*

Q13 $\frac{2}{7} \times \frac{3}{5} = \frac{2 \times 3}{7 \times 5} = \frac{6}{35}$

$\frac{2}{3} \div 3 = \frac{2}{3 \times 3} = \frac{2}{9}$
(1 mark for both correct)

Q14 3k + 14 = 32
3k = 32 − 14 = 18
k = 18 ÷ 3 = **6** *(1 mark)*

MLHW21